MATH TRAILBLAZERS™

Grade
4

Discovery Assignment Book

Second Edition

A Mathematical Journey Using Science and Language Arts

KENDALL/HUNT PUBLISHING COMPANY
4050 Westmark Drive   Dubuque, Iowa 52002

A TIMS® Curriculum
University of Illinois at Chicago

MATH TRAILBLAZERS™

Dedication

This book is dedicated to
the children and teachers
who let us see the magic
in their classrooms
and to our families who
wholeheartedly
supported us while we
searched for
ways to make it happen.

The TIMS Project

 UIC The University of Illinois at Chicago

The original edition was based on work supported by the National Science Foundation under grant No. MDR 9050226 and the University of Illinois at Chicago. Any opinions, findings, and conclusions or recommendations expressed in this publication are those of the authors and do not necessarily reflect the views of the granting agencies.

Table of Contents

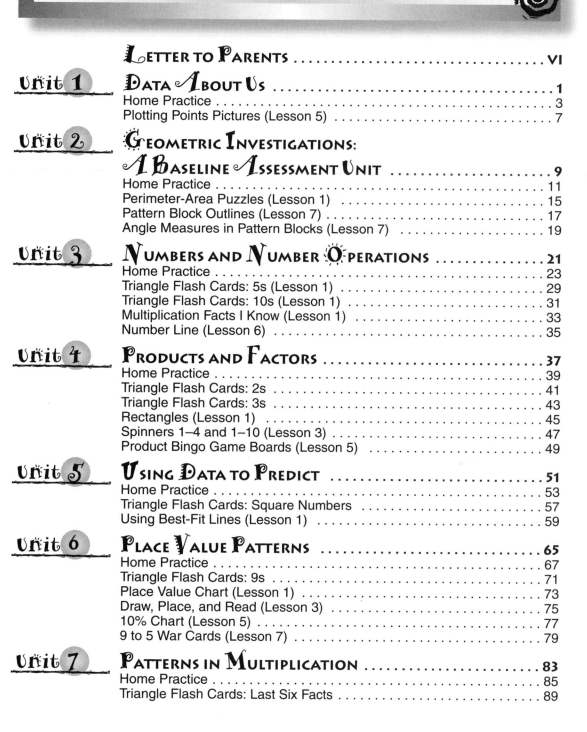

Additional student pages may be found in the *Unit Resource Guide, Student Guide,* or the *Adventure Book.*

Table of Contents

Additional student pages may be found in the *Unit Resource Guide, Student Guide,* or the *Adventure Book.*

iv

Table of Contents

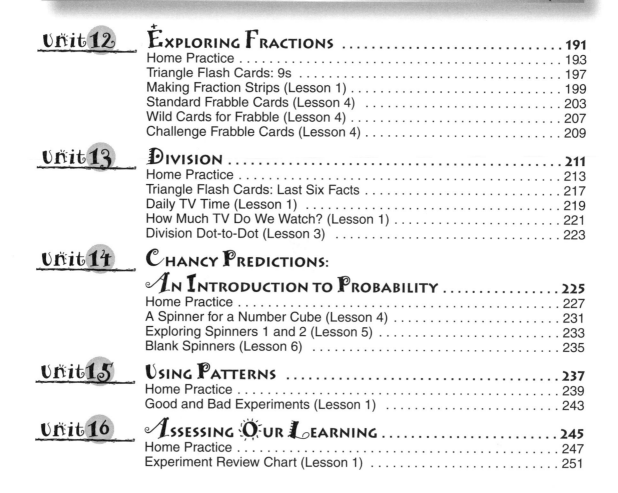
Additional student pages may be found in the *Unit Resource Guide, Student Guide,* or the *Adventure Book.*

Letter to Parents

Dear Parents,

Math Trailblazers™ is based on the ideas that mathematics is best learned through solving many different kinds of problems and that all children deserve a challenging mathematics curriculum. The program provides a careful balance of concepts and skills. Traditional arithmetic skills and procedures are covered through their repeated use in problems and through distributed practice. *Math Trailblazers,* however, offers much more. Students using this program will become proficient problem solvers, will know when and how to apply the mathematics they have learned, and will be able to clearly communicate their mathematical knowledge. Computation, measurement, geometry, data collection and analysis, estimation, graphing, patterns and relationships, mental arithmetic, and simple algebraic ideas are all an integral part of the curriculum. They will see connections between the mathematics learned in school and the mathematics used in everyday life. And, they will enjoy and value the work they do in mathematics.

The *Student Guide* is only one component of *Math Trailblazers.* Additional material and lessons are contained in the *Discovery Assignment Book,* the *Adventure Book,* and in the teacher's *Unit Resource Guides.* If you have questions about the program, we encourage you to speak with your child's teacher.

This curriculum was built around national recommendations for improving mathematics instruction in American schools and the research that supported those recommendations. The first edition was extensively tested with thousands of children in dozens of classrooms over five years of development. In preparing this second edition, we have benefited from the comments and suggestions of hundreds of teachers and children who have used the curriculum. *Math Trailblazers* reflects our view of a complete and well-balanced mathematics program that will prepare children for the 21st century—a world in which mathematical skills will be important in most occupations and mathematical reasoning will be essential for acting as an informed citizen in a democratic society. We hope that you enjoy this exciting approach to learning mathematics and that you watch your child's mathematical abilities grow throughout the year.

Philip Wagreich

Philip Wagreich
Professor, Department of Mathematics, Statistics, and Computer Science
Director, Institute for Mathematics and Science Education
The *Math Trailblazers* Team
Teaching Integrated Mathematics and Science (TIMS) Project
University of Illinois at Chicago

vi

Unit 1

Data About Us

	Student Guide	Discovery Assignment Book	Adventure Book	Unit Resource Guide*
Lesson 1				
Getting to Know Room 204	◎			
Lesson 2				
Getting to Know Room 204 a Little Better	◎			
Lesson 3				
An Average Activity	◎			
Lesson 4				
The Four Servants			◎	
Lesson 5				
Arm Span vs. Height	◎	◎		◎
Lesson 6				
Solving Problems About Room 204	◎			

Unit Resource Guide pages are from the teacher materials.

Unit 1: Home Practice

Part 1 Practice

Solve the following addition problems. Try to solve the problems without paper and pencil. Be prepared to share your solution strategies.

1. 8 + 3 + 5 = _____

2. 9 + 7 + 5 = _____

3. 6 + 8 + 6 = _____

4. 4 + 8 + 9 = _____

5. 70 + 30 = _____

6. 60 + 20 + 30 = _____

7. 50 + 70 = _____

8. 30 + 50 + 70 = _____

9. 20 + 85 = _____

10. 10 + 80 + 15 = _____

Part 2 Variables and Values

Look around your home and find four variables. Find two numerical variables and two categorical variables. Then, name some values for each of your variables. Be prepared to discuss and compare your findings. For example: Type of drinks is a categorical variable. Some values for this variable are iced tea, milk, and fruit juice.

1. Variable: _____ numerical or categorical (circle one)

   Values of your variable:

2. Variable: _____ numerical or categorical (circle one)

   Values of your variable:

3. Variable: _____ numerical or categorical (circle one)

   Values of your variable:

4. Variable: _____ numerical or categorical (circle one)

   Values of your variable:

Part 3 Finding the Median

1. Mr. Lewis's fourth-grade class did an experiment with colored candies. Five students took a handful of candy. They pulled 12, 6, 5, 3, and 7 pieces of candy. What is the median number of candies pulled? Show how you decided.

2. Lee Yah measured the hand lengths of the people in her family. Her grandmother's hand measured 15 cm in length. Her two sisters' hand lengths were 12 cm and 10 cm. Her mother's hand length was 14 cm. Her father's hand length was 18 cm. Lee Yah's hand measured 12 cm. What is the median hand length in Lee Yah's family? Show how you decided.

3. The fourth-grade soccer team at Bessie Coleman School practices after school. This week they practiced for 45 minutes on Monday, 30 minutes on Tuesday, an hour on Thursday, and 40 minutes on Friday. They skipped practice on Wednesday. What is the median number of minutes they practiced for the five days? Show how you decided.

4. Eight of Mrs. Dewey's students stayed after school to help her decorate her bulletin boards. She gave each student a box of raisins as a treat. Each student counted the number of raisins in his or her box. Here is their data: 23, 27, 22, 26, 21, 27, 25, and 23. Based on the students' data, what is the median number of raisins found in a box? Show how you decided.

Part 4 Measuring in Inches

You will need an inch ruler to complete this assignment. Estimate the length in inches of four objects in your home. Then, measure each object to the nearest inch. Complete the data table below.

Object	Estimate (in inches)	Actual (in inches)

Part 5 Inches and Centimeters

You will need a ruler that measures inches and centimeters for this part.

1. Which is longer, 1 centimeter or 1 inch? _____ Using a ruler, draw a line that is 1 centimeter long. Draw another line, 1 inch long. Label each line with its measurement.

2. Which is longer, 5 centimeters or 3 inches? _____ Using a ruler, draw a line that is 5 centimeters long. Draw another line, 3 inches long. Label each line with its measurement.

3. A. Which is longer, 40 centimeters or 13 inches? _____
   B. How did you decide?

Part 6 The Students in Room 204

Solve each of the following problems. Show how you solved each problem. If you need additional space, use a clean sheet of paper.

1. Ming said, "I collect baseball cards. If I collect 30 more, I'll have 250 cards." How many cards does Ming have now?

2. Keenya likes to listen to music while she practices her tumbling routines for gymnastics class. She listened to two complete cassette tapes while practicing today. There are about 10 songs on each tape, and each song is between 2 and 3 minutes long. About how long did Keenya practice?

3. Irma likes to read. She has two weeks to read the books she took out from the library. One book has 158 pages. The other book has 76 pages.

   A. How many pages are in the two books?

   B. If she reads about ten pages a day, can she finish the two books in two weeks?

4. Maya's family went on a three-day bike trip last week. They biked 36 miles on Friday, 33 on Saturday, and 45 on Sunday. How many miles did they bike in all?

5. It is 4:30 now. Nila's dinner will be ready at 5:15. Nila wants to play her new computer basketball game for twenty minutes. However, she needs fifteen minutes to walk the dog and about seven minutes to set the table. Will Nila be ready for dinner on time? Explain your answer.

6. Write a word problem that describes something about yourself. Write the answer and show how you solved the problem.

Plotting Points Pictures

Number the axes on a sheet of *Centimeter Grid Paper* by ones. Plot the data shown below. Use a ruler to connect the points with lines as you plot each point. When the data table says stop, start at the next new point, but do not connect the previous point.

Picture 1

Horizontal Axis	Vertical Axis
1	1
2	3
4	5
5	7
6	8
5	6
5	4
3	3
2	1
4	2
6	2
7	5
8	3
7	0
10	3
9	6
10	4
12	2
15	1
14	3
12	4
11	5
10	7
12	5
14	5
15	7
15	11

Horizontal Axis	Vertical Axis
14	13
12	13
10	11
11	13
15	15
10	15
9	13
8	14
8	16
10	17
12	16
15	17
12	18
10	19
7	18
6	16
6	14
7	12
6	13
4	17
2	19
0	19
3	16
5	12
6	11
4	12
2	12

Horizontal Axis	Vertical Axis
0	10
0	5
2	9
3	10
5	9
4	8
3	6
1	4
1	1
S T O P	
12	12
10	10
10	8
12	6
S T O P	
13	11
12	11
12	10
13	10
13	11
S T O P	
13	8
12	8
12	7
13	7
13	8
S T O P	

Name _____   Date _____

Number the axes on a sheet of *Centimeter Grid Paper* by tens. The horizontal axis must go up to 150 and the vertical axis must go up to 200. Plot the data shown below on grid paper. Use a ruler to connect the points with lines as you plot each point.

Picture 2

Horizontal Axis	Vertical Axis
45	0
85	0
125	40
130	80
70	80
70	90
150	90
70	180
105	185
70	200
70	80
60	80
60	200
0	90
60	90
60	80
0	80
5	40
45	0

Arm Span vs. Height

Unit 2

GEOMETRIC INVESTIGATIONS: A BASELINE ASSESSMENT UNIT

	Student Guide	Discovery Assignment Book	Adventure Book	Unit Resource Guide*
Lesson 1				
Investigating Perimeter and Area	◎	◎		
Lesson 2				
Perimeter vs. Length	◎			
Lesson 3				
Letter to Myrna				◎
Lesson 4				
Helipads for Antopolis	◎			
Lesson 5				
Portfolios	◎			
Lesson 6				
Angles	◎			◎
Lesson 7				
Angles in Pattern Blocks	◎	◎		

Unit Resource Guide pages are from the teacher materials.

Perimeter-Area Puzzles

Use square-inch tiles to measure the perimeter and area for each shape.
Record your measurements on the data table at the bottom of the next page.

A.

B.

C.

D.

E.

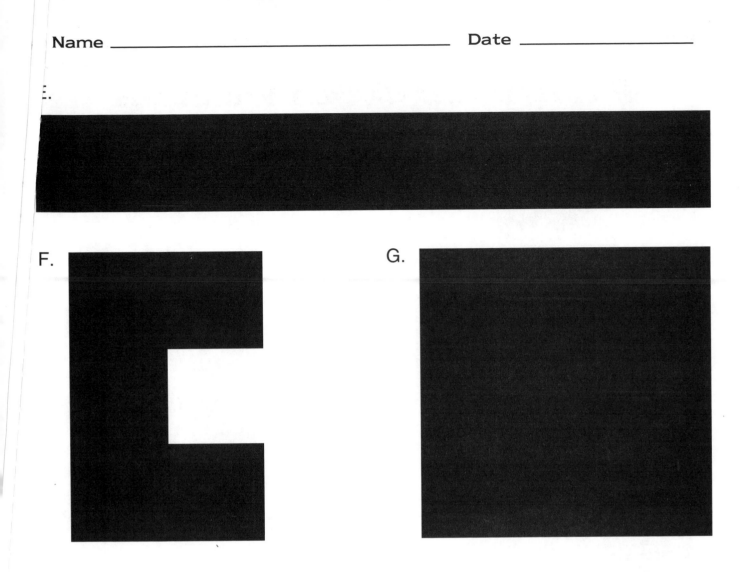

F.

G.

Shape	Perimeter in Inches	Area in Sq Inches
A		
B		
C		
D		
E		
F		
G		

Pattern Block Outlines

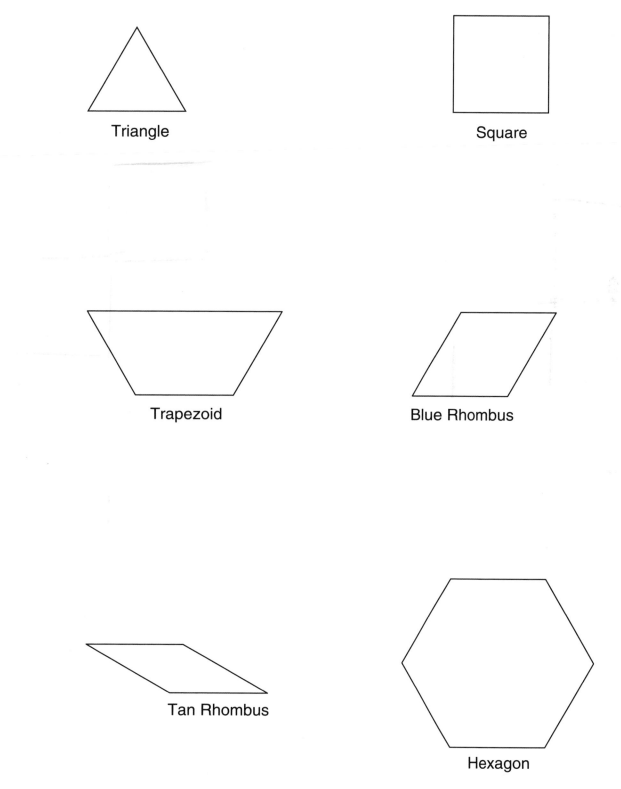

Triangle

Square

Trapezoid

Blue Rhombus

Tan Rhombus

Hexagon

Unit 3

Numbers and Number Operations

	Student Guide	Discovery Assignment Book	Adventure Book	Unit Resource Guide*
Lesson 1				
Multiplying and Dividing with 5s and 10s				
Lesson 2				
Roman Numerals				
Lesson 3				
Place Value				
Lesson 4				
The TIMS Candy Company				
Lesson 5				
Addition and Subtraction				
Lesson 6				
What's Below Zero?				
Lesson 7				
At the Hardware Store				

Unit Resource Guide pages are from the teacher materials.

Unit 3: Home Practice

Part 1 Triangle Flash Cards: 5s and 10s

Study for the quiz on the multiplication facts for the fives and tens. Take home your *Triangle Flash Cards: 5s* and *10s* and your list of facts you need to study.

Here's how to use the flash cards. Ask a family member to choose one flash card at a time. He or she should cover the corner containing the highest number. This number will be the answer to a multiplication problem. Multiply the two uncovered numbers.

Study the math facts in small groups. Choose eight to ten facts to study each night. Your teacher will tell you when the quiz on the fives and tens will be.

Part 2 Addition and Subtraction

Use paper and pencil to solve the following problems.

1. $\begin{array}{r} 644 \\ +\ 53 \end{array}$	2. $\begin{array}{r} 76 \\ +29 \end{array}$	3. $\begin{array}{r} 386 \\ -\ 21 \end{array}$	4. $\begin{array}{r} 196 \\ -\ 77 \end{array}$
5. $\begin{array}{r} 938 \\ -449 \end{array}$	6. $\begin{array}{r} 4015 \\ +\ 488 \end{array}$	7. $\begin{array}{r} 5048 \\ -\ 274 \end{array}$	8. $\begin{array}{r} 4653 \\ +5664 \end{array}$

Choose one problem. Be ready to explain how you can tell if the answer is reasonable.

Part 3 People and Prices

1. Some of the workers at the TIMS Candy Company went to the fruit stand for lunch. Maggie bought a plum for 29¢ and an apple for 39¢. If she pays with $1.00, how much change should she receive?

2. A comic book at the used book sale costs 5¢. Special edition comic books cost 10¢ each. How much does Shannon need to pay if she wants to purchase 3 regular comic books and 4 special edition comic books?

3. Roberto's father is a salesman for the TIMS Candy Company. At the end of the year, Roberto's father earned a bonus of $565. This was $180 more than last year's bonus.

   A. How much did Roberto's father receive as a bonus last year?

   B. How can you be sure your answer is reasonable?

4. Ana went to the movies. She only had dimes with her. If the movie costs $1.75, how many dimes does she need to give the cashier? Explain.

5. Jessie went with her family to a two-day fall festival. On the first day, 4367 adults attended the fest and 4587 children attended.

   A. The newspaper reported the actual attendance. Calculate the actual attendance for the first day.

   B. About how many more people need to attend on the second day to reach a total of 10,000 people at the festival? Explain.

Part 4 Fact Families

For each fact given, write the other three members of the same fact family.

A. $6 \times 5 = 30$

_____

_____

_____

B. $90 \div 10 = 9$

_____

_____

_____

C. $15 \div 5 = 3$

_____

_____

_____

D. $5 \times 9 = 45$

_____

_____

_____

E. $5 \times 10 = 50$

_____

_____

_____

Part 5 More Fact Families

Solve the problems below and complete the number sentences for the related facts.

A. $10 \times 10 = $ _____

_____ $\div 10 = 10$

B. $10 \div 5 = $ _____

_____ $\times 5 = 10$

$5 \times $ _____ $= $ _____

_____ $\div$ _____ $= 5$

C. _____ $\div 10 = 3$

_____ $\div 3 = $ _____

$3 \times $ _____ $= $ _____

_____ $\times 3 = $ _____

D. $6 \times $ _____ $= 30$

_____ $\times 6 = $ _____

$30 \div 6 = $ _____

$30 \div $ _____ $= $ _____

E. $7 \times 10 = $ _____

_____ $\times 7 = $ _____

_____ $\div 7 = $ _____

_____ $\div$ _____ $= $ _____

F. $1 \times 5 = $ _____

$5 \times $ _____ $= $ _____

$5 \div $ _____ $= $ _____

_____ $\div$ _____ $= $ _____

Part 6 Drawing Angles

1. Draw an angle that is about 45 degrees. Is this angle acute or obtuse?

2. Draw an angle that is more than 90 degrees but less than 180 degrees. Is this angle acute or obtuse?

3. Draw five different size angles. Draw them in order from smallest to largest.

4. Use a ruler to draw a five-sided shape (a pentagon) with one right angle.

Part 7 Arithmetic Review

Use paper and pencil or mental math to solve these problems. Remember to do a quick estimate first and then look at your answer to make sure it makes sense.

1. 123
    + 537

2. 672
    − 253

3. 303
    + 497

4. 897
    + 481

5. 460
    − 255

6. 461
    791
    + 23

7. Explain how you solved Question 3.

8. Explain how you can solve Question 4 using base-ten shorthand.

9. Explain your estimation strategy for Question 6.

Triangle Flash Cards: 5s

- Work with a partner. Each partner cuts out the flash cards below.
- Your partner chooses one card at a time and covers the shaded corner.
- Multiply the two uncovered numbers.
- Divide the used cards into three piles: those that you know and can answer quickly, those that you can figure out, and those that you need to learn.
- Practice the last two piles again. Then, make a list of the facts you need to practice at home.
- Repeat the directions for your partner.

Triangle Flash Cards: 10s

- Work with a partner. Each partner cuts out the 9 flash cards below.
- Your partner chooses one card at a time and covers the shaded corner.
- Multiply the two uncovered numbers.
- Divide the used cards into three piles: those that you know and can answer quickly, those that you can figure out, and those that you need to learn.
- Practice the last two piles again. Then, make a list of the facts you need to practice at home.
- Repeat the directions for your partner.

Multiplication Facts I Know

- Circle the facts you know well.
- Keep this table and use it to help you multiply.
- As you learn more facts, you may circle them too.

×	0	1	2	3	4	5	6	7	8	9	10
0	0	0	0	0	0	0	0	0	0	0	0
1	0	1	2	3	4	5	6	7	8	9	10
2	0	2	4	6	8	10	12	14	16	18	20
3	0	3	6	9	12	15	18	21	24	27	30
4	0	4	8	12	16	20	24	28	32	36	40
5	0	5	10	15	20	25	30	35	40	45	50
6	0	6	12	18	24	30	36	42	48	54	60
7	0	7	14	21	28	35	42	49	56	63	70
8	0	8	16	24	32	40	48	56	64	72	80
9	0	9	18	27	36	45	54	63	72	81	90
10	0	10	20	30	40	50	60	70	80	90	100

Number Line

Cut out the number line pieces below and tape or glue them at the tabs.

Unit 4

Products and Factors

	Student Guide	Discovery Assignment Book	Adventure Book	Unit Resource Guide*
Lesson 1				
Multiplication and Rectangles	◎	◎		
Lesson 2				
Factors	◎			
Lesson 3				
Floor Tiler	◎	◎		
Lesson 4				
Prime Factors	◎			◎
Lesson 5				
Product Bingo	◎	◎		
Lesson 6				
Multiplying to Solve Problems	◎			

Unit Resource Guide pages are from the teacher materials.

Unit 4: Home Practice

Part 1 *Triangle Flash Cards: 2s and 3s*

Study for the quiz on the multiplication facts for the 2s and 3s. Take home your *Triangle Flash Cards: 2s* and *3s* and your list of facts you need to study.

Here's how to use the flash cards. Ask a family member to choose one flash card at a time. He or she should cover the corner containing the highest number. This number will be the answer to a multiplication fact. Multiply the two uncovered numbers.

Study the math facts in small groups. Choose eight to ten facts to study each night. Your teacher will tell you when the quiz on the 2s and 3s will be.

Part 2 Multiplication: Factors, Multiples, Primes, and Squares

To solve the following problems, you may use your *Student Guide* as a reference. See Unit 4 Lessons 1, 2, and 4.

1. Is 34 a multiple of 2? Explain why or why not.

2. Is 3 a factor of 35? Explain why or why not.

3. Name 10 numbers that are multiples of 2.

4. Name 10 numbers that have 3 as a factor.

5. Is 7 a prime number? Why or why not?

6. **A.** $5^2 =$ **B.** $10^2 =$

   C. $2^2 =$ **D.** $3^2 =$

Part 3 Working at the Grocery Store

Choose an appropriate tool to help you solve each of the problems. Use a picture, paper and pencil, or a calculator. Show how you solved each problem.

1. Keenya's sister, Shenika, works at a grocery store. Today she is stocking shelves. She stacks soup cans three cans high. If she makes 6 stacks, how many soup cans will she shelve?

2. Shenika brings in some shopping carts from the parking lot. She makes 4 rows of carts. She tries to place the same number of carts in each row. If she brings in 17 carts, how many carts can she place in each row?

3. Shenika gets paid six dollars an hour. Last week she worked 15 hours. How much did she earn?

4. When Shenika works the cash register on a Saturday, she works nonstop. In the express line, customers may purchase only 10 items or less. When working the express line, she can ring up about 5 customers in 15 minutes. If she works a 6-hour day, about how many customers can she serve?

5. The grocery bill for one of Shenika's customers is $15.52. The customer gives Shenika $20.02. How much change should the customer receive?

6. Grapes are on sale for 69¢ a pound. How much do 3 pounds of grapes cost?

7. For every $3 a customer spends at the grocery store, he or she gets a stamp that can be used for purchasing dishes. One customer bought groceries for herself and an elderly neighbor. The two separate bills were $43 and $28. How many stamps should this customer receive for herself and her neighbor?

PRODUCTS AND FACTORS

Triangle Flash Cards: 2s

- Work with a partner. Each partner cuts out the flash cards.
- Your partner chooses one card at a time and covers the shaded corner containing the highest number.
- Multiply the two uncovered numbers.
- Divide the used cards into three piles: those that you know and can answer quickly, those that you can figure out, and those that you need to learn.
- Practice the last two piles again. Then, make a list of the facts you need to practice at home.
- Repeat the directions for your partner.

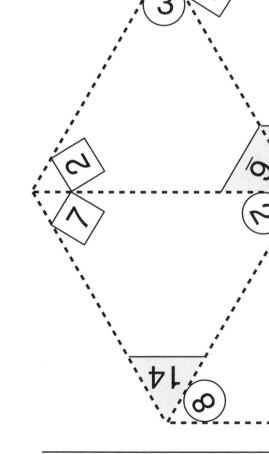

Triangle Flash Cards: 3s

- Work with a partner. Each partner cuts out the flash cards.
- Your partner chooses one card at a time and covers the shaded corner containing the highest number.
- Multiply the two uncovered numbers.
- Divide the used cards into three piles: those that you know and can answer quickly, those that you can figure out, and those that you need to learn.
- Practice the last two piles again. Then, make a list of the facts you need to practice at home.
- Repeat the directions for your partner.

Name _____ Date _____

Rectangles

1	2	3	4	5	6	7	8	9	10	11	12	13
14	15	16	17	18	19	20	21	22	23	24	25	

Product Bingo Game Boards

Board 1

40	72	10	35
42	28	20	27
15	45	P	6
30	48	14	56

Board 3

8	24	27	54
20	12	21	32
36	P	14	45
63	18	72	16

Board 2

9	P	22	81
64	13	25	32
15	14	56	29
7	10	4	49

Board 4

4	45	25	81
49	56	6	32
9	64	P	10
15	8	42	48

Unit 5

USING DATA TO PREDICT

	Student Guide	Discovery Assignment Book	Adventure Book	Unit Resource Guide*
Lesson 1				
Predictions from Graphs	◉	◉		
Lesson 2				
Another Average Activity	◉			
Lesson 3				
The Meaning of the ...	◉			◉
Lesson 4				
Bouncing Ball	◉			
Lesson 5				
Two Heads Are Better Than One			◉	
Lesson 6				
Professor Peabody Invents a Ball				◉
Lesson 7				
Speeds at the Indianapolis 500	◉			
Lesson 8				
Midterm Test				◉

Unit Resource Guide pages are from the teacher materials.

Unit 5: Home Practice

Part 1 Triangle Flash Cards: Square Numbers

Study for the quiz on the multiplication facts for the square numbers. Take home your *Triangle Flash Cards: Square Numbers* and your list of facts you need to study.

Here's how to use the flash cards. Ask a family member to choose one flash card at a time. Your helper should cover the corner containing the highest number. This number will be the answer to a multiplication fact. Multiply the two uncovered numbers.

Your teacher will tell you when the quiz on the square numbers will be.

Part 2 Time and Roman Numerals

A table of Roman numerals is provided in Unit 3 Lesson 2 of your *Student Guide*. You may use it as a reference.

1. Skip count by 3s from 3 to 30 using Roman numerals.

III	VI		XII			XXI			
3	6	9		15					

2. Skip count by 20s from 20 to 200 using Roman numerals.

XX	XL				CXX				
20	40					140			

3. What time does each clock show?

A.   B.   C.

Part 3 Factor Trees and Exponents

Write each of the following numbers as a product of prime numbers. If you need more room to show your work, use a separate sheet of paper.

1. 52

2. 85

3. 224

4. Write each of the following using exponents. Then, find each product.

A. $4 \times 4 \times 2$ B. $5 \times 2 \times 5$ C. $2 \times 3 \times 2 \times 2$

Part 4 What's Missing?

The letter n stands for a missing number. What number must n be in each number sentence to make the sentence true?

1. $750 + 150 = n$ 2. $839 + 102 = n$ 3. $1034 - 40 = n$

4. $2 + n = 100$ 5. $16 - n = 8$ 6. $n + 21 = 42$

7. $n - 25 = 50$ 8. $11 + n = 24$ 9. $93 - n = 23$

10. $70 - n = 40$ 11. $71 - n = 40$ 12. $15 - n = 9$

Part 5 Making Predictions from a Graph

The data below shows the winning times women swam the 200-meter backstroke at the Olympics. The winning times are given to the nearest second.

Time (in years)	Time (in seconds)
1968	145
1972	139
1976	133
1980	132
1984	132
1988	129
1992	127
1996	128
2000	128

1. Plot the data on a piece of *Centimeter Graph Paper.* Scale the vertical axis to 150 seconds. Scale the horizontal axis by fours, from 1960 to 2008. Then, answer Questions 2–7. Use a separate sheet of paper if you need to.

2. **A.** What variable did you plot on the horizontal axis on the graph? _____

   B. Is this variable numerical or categorical? _____

3. What variable did you plot on the vertical axis? _____

4. About how many minutes was the winning time for the 200-meter backstroke in 1992? _____

5. Do the points lie close to a line? _____ If they do, use a ruler to draw a best-fit line through the points.

6. Describe the graph. What does it tell you about the history of the 200-meter backstroke?

7. Can you use this graph to predict the winning time for the women's 200-meter backstroke in the year 2008? _____ If so, how? What is your prediction?

Part 6 Bouncing Balls

Grace and her lab partner Michael experimented with 3 kinds of balls to find out which one bounced highest. They dropped each type of ball from the same height. Here is their data.

T Type of Ball	H Bounce Height (in cm)			
	Trial 1	Trial 2	Trial 3	Median
Basketball	43	41	45	
Kickball	69	65	67	
Tennis Ball	52	51	51	

1. Find the median bounce height for each type of ball. Complete the table with your answers.

2. What is the manipulated variable? Is it a categorical or numerical variable?

3. What is the responding variable? Is it a categorical or numerical variable?

4. Think about these questions before you graph the median bounce height for each type of ball.
   - What variable will you put on the horizontal axis?
   - What variable will you put on the vertical axis?
   - How will you scale and label the axes?
   - What type of graph is appropriate? A point graph or a bar graph?

USING DATA TO PREDICT

Triangle Flash Cards: Square Numbers

- Work with a partner. Each partner cuts out the flash cards.
- Your partner chooses one card at a time and covers the shaded corner containing the highest number.
- Multiply the two uncovered numbers.
- Sort the used cards into three piles: those that you know and can answer quickly, those that you can figure out, and those that you need to learn.
- Practice the last two piles again. Then, make a list of the facts you need to practice at home.
- Repeat the directions for your partner.

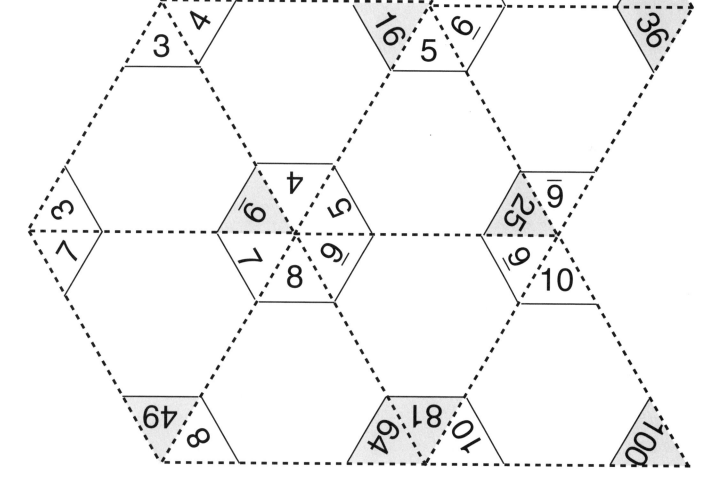

Using Best-Fit Lines

1. Each year, Mrs. Welch, a gym teacher at Bessie Coleman School, records the number of sit-ups each student can do. Nila used her data to make a graph which shows the number of sit-ups she could do each year.

   A. Describe the graph.

   B. If you read the graph from left to right, do the points go uphill or downhill?

   C. What does the graph tell you about the number of sit-ups Nila can do?

   D. Do the points lie close to a straight line? If so, use a ruler to draw a best-fit line.

   E. If possible, predict the number of sit-ups Nila will be able to do when she is 12.

   F. Does knowing Nila's age help you predict the number of sit-ups she can do?

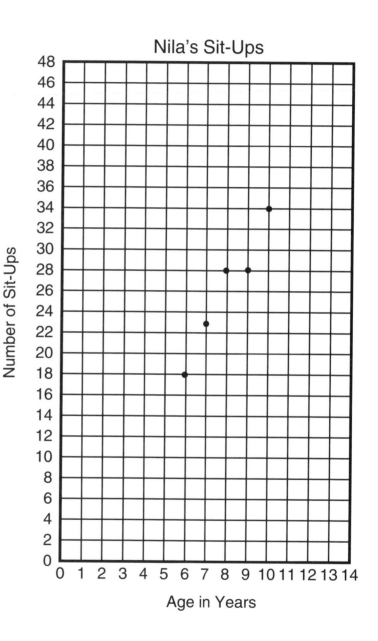

Nila's Sit-Ups

---

2. Mrs. Welch also records each student's best times for running a mile. John graphed his best times.

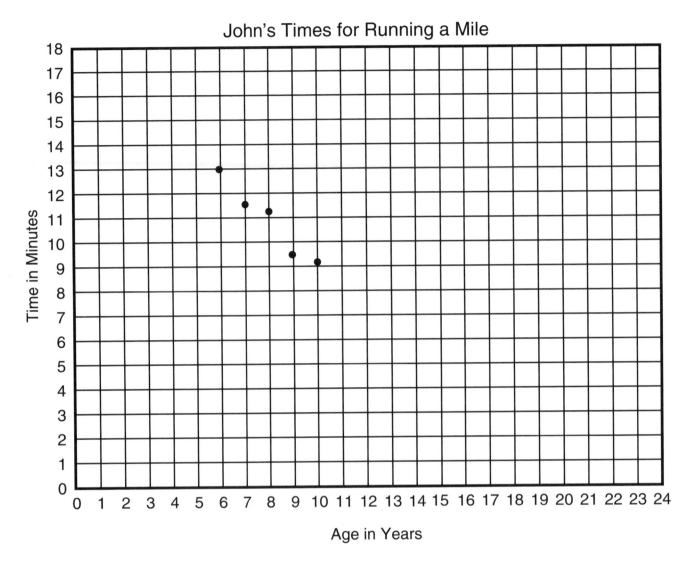

John's Times for Running a Mile

(Graph: y-axis "Time in Minutes" from 0 to 18; x-axis "Age in Years" from 0 to 24. Plotted points are approximately at age 6/13 minutes, age 7/11.6 minutes, age 8/11.3 minutes, age 9/9.5 minutes, age 10/9.3 minutes.)

A. Describe the graph.

B. Do the points tend to go uphill or downhill?

C. Do the points lie close to a straight line? If so, use a ruler to draw a best-fit line.

D. If possible, predict how long it will take John to run a mile when he is 12.

E. If possible, predict how long it will take John to run a mile when he is 18.

F. Does knowing John's age help you predict his time for running the mile?

3. A fourth-grade class recorded the month each student was born and the number of letters in each student's name. Using the data, the class made the following graph.

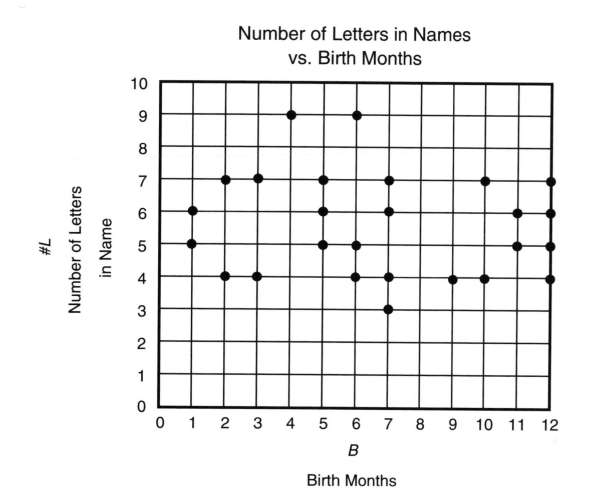

Number of Letters in Names
vs. Birth Months

Birth Months

A. Describe the graph.

B. Do the points lie close to a straight line? If so, use a ruler to draw a best-fit line.

C. Does knowing the month a student was born help you predict the number of letters in his or her name?

D. If possible, predict the number of letters in a student's name if he or she was born in August (the eighth month).

4. A cookie company wants all the cookies from the factory to be the same. Here is a graph made by a cookie inspector.

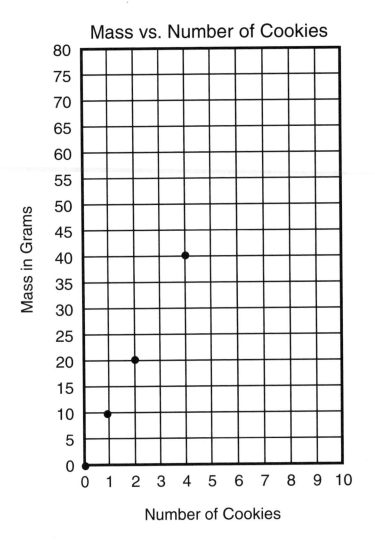

A. Describe the graph.

B. Do the points lie close to a straight line? If so, use a ruler to draw a best-fit line.

C. If possible, predict the mass of 3 cookies.

D. If possible, predict the mass of 5 cookies.

E. Did you use interpolation or extrapolation to answer Question 4C?

5. Doctors measure the head circumference of babies to track their growth.

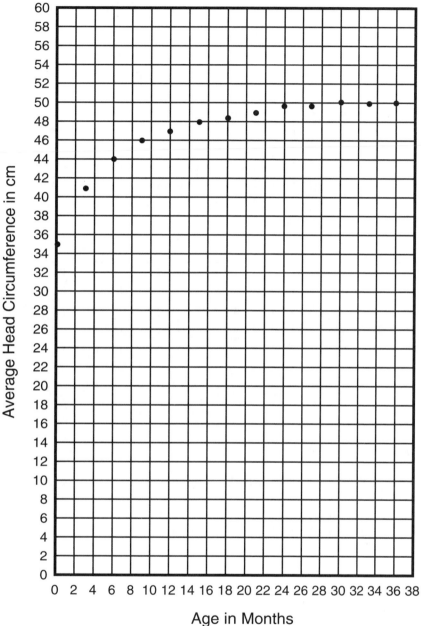

Head Circumference of Babies

Average Head Circumference in cm (y-axis)

Age in Months (x-axis)

A. Describe the graph.

B. If the points lie close to a line, use a ruler to draw a best-fit line.

C. If possible, predict the head circumference of a baby who is four months old.

6. The winning times for the women's Olympic breaststroke swimming competition are shown in this graph.

Winning Times for the
Women's Olympic Breaststroke

A. Describe the graph.

B. If the points lie close to a line, use a ruler to draw a best-fit line.

7. Look back at the graphs in Questions 1–6. Which graph gives the most accurate predictions? Explain your choice.

Unit 6
Place Value Patterns

	Student Guide	Discovery Assignment Book	Adventure Book	Unit Resource Guide*
Lesson 1				
Newswire	◉	◉		
Lesson 2				
Doubles	◉			
Lesson 3				
Big Base-Ten Pieces	◉	◉		
Lesson 4				
News Number Line	◉			
Lesson 5				
Close Enough	◉	◉		
Lesson 6				
Using Estimation	◉			◉
Lesson 7				
9 to 5 War	◉	◉		

Unit Resource Guide pages are from the teacher materials.

Unit 6: Home Practice

Part 1 *Triangle Flash Cards: 9s*

Study for the quiz on the multiplication facts for the nines. Take home your *Triangle Flash Cards: 9s* and your list of facts you need to study.

Here's how to use the flash cards. Ask a family member to choose one flash card at a time. He or she should cover the corner containing the highest number. This number will be the answer to a multiplication fact. Multiply the two uncovered numbers.

Your teacher will tell you when the quiz on the 9s will be.

Part 2 Mixed-Up Multiplication Tables

1. Complete the table. Then, describe any patterns you see.

×	2	3	5	9	10
4					
6		18			
7					
8					

2. *n* stands for a missing number. Find the missing number in each number sentence.

   A. $n \times 7 = 14$ **B.** $3 \times n = 24$ **C.** $n \times 4 = 16$ **D.** $n \times 8 = 80$

   E. $9 \times n = 63$ **F.** $n \times 8 = 64$ **G.** $4 \times n = 36$ **H.** $n \times 5 = 30$

Part 3 Addition and Subtraction Practice

Use paper and pencil to solve the following problems. Use estimation to decide if your answers make sense. Explain your estimation strategy for F.

A. 4506
  + 8753

B. 5388
  + 9078

C. 9054
  − 2408

D. 7617
  − 4543

E. 3940
  + 6963

F. 10,415
  − 7593

Part 4 Using Estimation

The following table lists the number of people who immigrated to the United States from various countries in 2000. Use the information in the table to estimate the answers to the questions below. Use a separate sheet of paper to show what convenient numbers you chose to work with.

Country	Number of Immigrants	Country	Number of Immigrants
Canada	21,475	Mexico	171,748
China	41,861	Philippines	40,587
Dominican Republic	17,441	Romania	6,521
El Salvador	22,332	United Kingdom	14,532
India	39,072	Vietnam	25,340

1. Most immigrants came from which five countries listed in the table? List the countries and their population. List the populations in order from largest to smallest.

2. About how many more people immigrated from Mexico than from China?

3. About how many people immigrated from Canada and Mexico combined?

4. The number of immigrants from El Salvador is about the same as the number from which other country?

5. About how many more people came from India than Romania?

6. In 2000, the number of immigrants from all countries totaled about 850,000 people. About how many immigrants are reported in the table above? (*Hint:* Use a calculator to help you with your estimation.)

Triangle Flash Cards: 9s

- Work with a partner. Each partner cuts out the flash cards.
- Your partner chooses one card at a time and covers the shaded corner.
- Multiply the two uncovered numbers.
- Divide the used cards into three piles: those that you know and can answer quickly, those that you can figure out, and those that you need to learn.
- Practice the last two piles again. Then, make a list of the facts you need to practice at home.
- Repeat the directions for your partner.

Draw, Place, and Read

This game can be played with 2 to 30 players. One player is the caller. You will need 10 cards numbered 0–9. If you have a large group, the game can be played with teams. Follow these directions:

1. Choose one person to be the caller. For each round, the caller will draw seven numbers. Decide ahead of time if the caller will replace each number after it has been recorded or if each number will be used only once in each round.

2. After each draw, players record the digit that was drawn in any column on the first row of the place value chart below. Once a digit has been recorded, it cannot be moved.

3. After all seven draws, the person who makes and reads the highest number earns a point. Move to the next row on the place value chart for the next round.

As an extra challenge, you can agree to use 8 or 9 draws instead of 7 for each round.

Millions' Period			Thousands' Period			Ones' Period		

10% Chart

Name on Jar	Object	N Actual Number	N ÷ 10	10% of the Number	Range

9 to 5 War Cards

9	9	9	9
9 to 5 War	9 to 5 War	9 to 5 War	9 to 5 War
9	5	5	5
9 to 5 War	9 to 5 War	9 to 5 War	9 to 5 War
5	5		
9 to 5 War	9 to 5 War		

9 to 5 War Cards

| 9 | 9 | 9 | 9 |
| 9 to 5 War | 9 to 5 War | 9 to 5 War | 9 to 5 War |

| 9 | 5 | 5 | 5 |
| 9 to 5 War | 9 to 5 War | 9 to 5 War | 9 to 5 War |

| 5 | 5 |
| 9 to 5 War | 9 to 5 War |

Unit 7
PATTERNS IN MULTIPLICATION

	Student Guide	Discovery Assignment Book	Adventure Book	Unit Resource Guide*
Lesson 1				
Order of Operations	◉			
Lesson 2				
Divisibility Rules	◉			◉
Lesson 3				
Oh, No! My Calculator Is Broken	◉			◉
Lesson 4				
Multiplying by 10s	◉			
Lesson 5				
Multiplication	◉			
Lesson 6				
Estimation	◉			
Lesson 7				
Multiplying Round Numbers	◉			◉
Lesson 8				
A Camping Trip	◉			

Unit Resource Guide pages are from the teacher materials.

Part 5 Multiplying by 10

1. Solve the following problems.

   A. $6 \times 70 =$ _____

   B. $8 \times 400 =$ _____

   C. $800 \times 6 =$ _____

   D. $7000 \times 4 =$ _____

   E. $800 \times 8 =$ _____

   F. $60 \times 4 =$ _____

2. Find what n must be to make each number sentence true.

   A. $60 \times n = 360$

   B. $n \times 5 = 350$

   C. $n \times 900 = 5400$

Part 6 More Multiplication

1. Solve the following problems using paper and pencil or mental math.

   A. $\begin{array}{r} 14 \\ \times 7 \\ \hline \end{array}$

   B. $\begin{array}{r} 700 \\ \times 40 \\ \hline \end{array}$

   C. $\begin{array}{r} 42 \\ \times 3 \\ \hline \end{array}$

   D. $\begin{array}{r} 35 \\ \times 8 \\ \hline \end{array}$

   E. $\begin{array}{r} 48 \\ \times 6 \\ \hline \end{array}$

   F. $\begin{array}{r} 600 \\ \times 300 \\ \hline \end{array}$

2. Use convenient numbers to estimate the following products.

   A. $50 \times 61 =$

   B. $89 \times 40 =$

   C. $397 \times 30 =$

Part 7 Groups and More Groups

1. Solve the following problems using paper and pencil or mental math.

   A. 53
       $\times 4$

   B. 38
       $\times 2$

   C. 77
       $\times 3$

   D. 65
       $\times 5$

2. Bessie Coleman School is holding a fund-raiser. The money earned will go towards buying new books for the school library. Jacob is in charge of pouring lemonade at the fund-raiser. He has 19 packages of paper cups. Each package has 20 cups. About how many cups does he have?

3. Lee Yah is in charge of selling hot dogs. She has 36 packages of hot dog buns at the start of the day. Each package has 8 buns. How many hot dogs can she sell?

4. Jacob is selling raffle tickets. One raffle ticket sells for $4.

   A. So far he has collected $160. How many raffle tickets did he sell?

   B. His goal is to collect $400. How many more raffle tickets must he sell to reach his goal?

5. Ten people can sit at one table for Bingo. There are 12 tables for Bingo. How many people can play Bingo at one time?

6. At the fund-raiser, a "meal deal" that includes a hot dog, drink, and chips costs $3. There are 96 students in the eighth grade at Bessie Coleman School. If each eighth grader buys one meal deal, how much money will the eighth grade class pay in all for their food?

Triangle Flash Cards: Last Six Facts

- Work with a partner. Each partner cuts out the flash cards.
- Your partner chooses one card at a time and covers the shaded corner containing the highest number.
- Multiply the two uncovered numbers.
- Divide the used cards into three piles: those that you know and can answer quickly, those that you can figure out, and those that you need to learn.
- Practice the last two piles again. Then, make a list of the facts you need to practice at home.
- Repeat the directions for your partner.

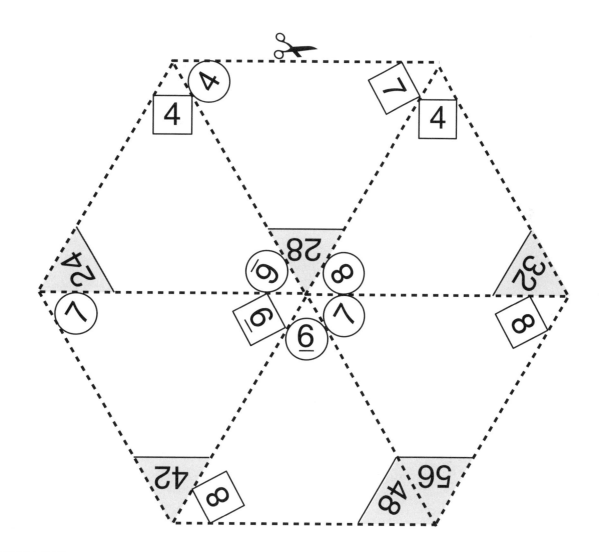

Unit 8

MEASURING UP: AN ASSESSMENT UNIT

	Student Guide	Discovery Assignment Book	Adventure Book	Unit Resource Guide*
Lesson 1				
Volume	◉	◉		
Lesson 2				
Fill It First	◉	◉		
Lesson 3				
Volume vs. Number	◉	◉		
Lesson 4				
Review Problems	◉			
Lesson 5				
Hour Walk				◉
Lesson 6				
Midyear Test				◉
Lesson 7				
Midyear Experiment and Portfolio Review	◉	◉		
Lesson 8				
Facts I Know: Multiplication and Division Facts	◉	◉		◉

*Unit Resource Guide pages are from the teacher materials.

Unit 8: Home Practice

Part 1 Triangle Flash Cards: Reviewing All the Facts

Study for the test on all the multiplication facts. Take home your *Triangle Flash Cards* for the 5s and 10s, 2s and 3s, square numbers, 9s, and the last six facts. Study the facts in small groups, about 8–10 facts each night.

Here's how to use the flash cards. Ask a family member to choose one flash card at a time. Your partner should cover the corner containing the highest number. This number will be the answer to a multiplication fact. Multiply the two uncovered numbers.

Separate the used cards into three piles: those facts you know and can answer quickly, those that you can figure out with a strategy, and those that you need to learn. Practice the last two piles again. Remember to concentrate on one small group of facts each night—about 8 to 10 facts. Also, remember to study only those facts you cannot answer correctly and quickly.

If you do not have your flash cards, create new ones for those facts that are not yet circled on your *Multiplication Facts I Know* chart. To create your flash cards, use the *Triangle Flash Cards Masters* that follow the Home Practice.

Your teacher will tell you when the test on all the multiplication facts will be.

Part 2 Number Relationships

1. **A.** Is 51 prime? Tell how you know.

    B. Is 53 prime? Tell how you know.

    C. Is 55 prime? Tell how you know.

2. **A.** Is 6 a factor of 96? How can you tell?

    B. Is 6 a factor of 116? How can you tell?

3. Make a factor tree to find the prime factors of 54.

Part 3 Performing Operations

1. Solve the following problems using paper and pencil or mental math.

   A. $459 + 769 =$

   B. $1078 + 5498 =$

   C. $7089 - 2793 =$

   D. $38 \times 5 =$

   E. $700 \times 90 =$

   F. $44 \times 6 =$

2. Shannon's dad is taking two night courses at a community college. Each course costs $86. Each of his two textbooks costs $45. How much does Shannon's dad have to pay to go to school?

3. In the 2001–2002 basketball season, Shaquille O'Neal of the Los Angeles Lakers averaged 27 points a game. If Shaquille played in 67 games, about how many points did he score?

4. In the 1992 presidential election, Bill Clinton received 44,908,254 votes. George Bush received 39,102,343 votes. About how many more votes did President Clinton get than Bush?

5. It takes the Earth about 365 days to revolve around the sun. Mercury's revolution around the sun takes 277 fewer days than the Earth's. How many days does it take Mercury to revolve around the sun?

Part 4 Arithmetic Review

1. Use paper and pencil or mental math to solve the following problems. Estimate to make sure your answers make sense.

   A. $6035 - 854 =$ **B.** $64 \times 8 =$ **C.** $47 \times 8 =$

   D. $437 + 579 + 902 =$ **E.** $3649 - 2089 =$ **F.** $82 \times 5 =$

2. Explain your estimation strategy for Question 1C.

3. Use estimation to answer Questions 3A and 3B. Record number sentences to show what convenient numbers you chose. Then, solve the problem in Question 3C.

   A. Maya has $10.00 to buy the following items: cereal for $3.28, milk for $2.89, and bread for $1.56. Estimate to see if she has enough money. If there is no sales tax, about how much change will Maya receive from her $10 bill or about how much more money will she need?

   B. Shannon has been given $15.00 to buy school supplies. She wants to buy 5 notebooks that cost $1.25 each, 10 pencils that cost 19 cents each, and 4 folders that cost 28 cents each. Estimate to see if she has enough money. About how much money will she have left? Or, how much extra will she need based on your estimation?

   C. Jerome's aunt gave him $20.00 for his birthday present. He purchased a shirt for $7.99, a cap for $2.60, and socks. After shopping, he had $5.67 left over. If no tax was paid, what was the exact cost of the socks? Look back at your answer. Is it reasonable?

Part 5   Base-Ten Shorthand

I. The bit is one whole. Label each of the following with its correct number.
    Then, put the numbers in order from least to greatest.

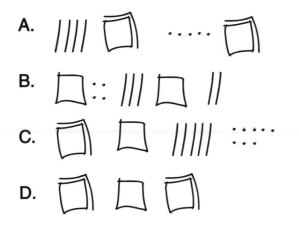

A.

B.

C.

D.

2. The following information, taken from the *1996 World Almanac,* shows the
    number of people employed in various occupations in the United States.

    Crafts people and those who repair things: 10,435,000 people
    Farming, forestry, and fishing: 1,430,000 people
    Machine operators and truck drivers: 14,001,000 people
    Professionals (accountants, doctors, lawyers,
        teachers, nurses):   23,247,000 people
    Sales people, technicians, administrative workers: 25,928,000 people
    Service jobs such as waiters, guards, and janitors: 9,104,000 people

    A. List the number of people employed in the different kinds of jobs in order
        from least to greatest.

    B. About 3,383,000 of the machine operators and truck drivers are women.
        About how many are men?

    C. About 12,082,000 of the professionals are men. About how many
        are women?

Triangle Flash Cards Master

- Make a flash card for each fact that is not circled on your *Multiplication Facts I Know* chart. Write the product in the shaded corner of each triangle. Write the factors in the other two corners. Then, cut out the flash cards.
- To quiz you on a multiplication fact, your partner covers the shaded number. Multiply the two uncovered numbers.
- Practice the last two piles again. Then, make a list of the facts you need to practice at home.
- Repeat the directions for your partner.

Triangle Flash Cards Master

- Make a flash card for each fact that is not circled on your *Multiplication Facts I Know* chart. Write the product in the shaded corner of each triangle. Write the factors in the other two corners. Then, cut out the flash cards.
- To quiz you on a multiplication fact, your partner covers the shaded number. Multiply the two uncovered numbers.
- Practice the last two piles again. Then, make a list of the facts you need to practice at home.
- Repeat the directions for your partner.

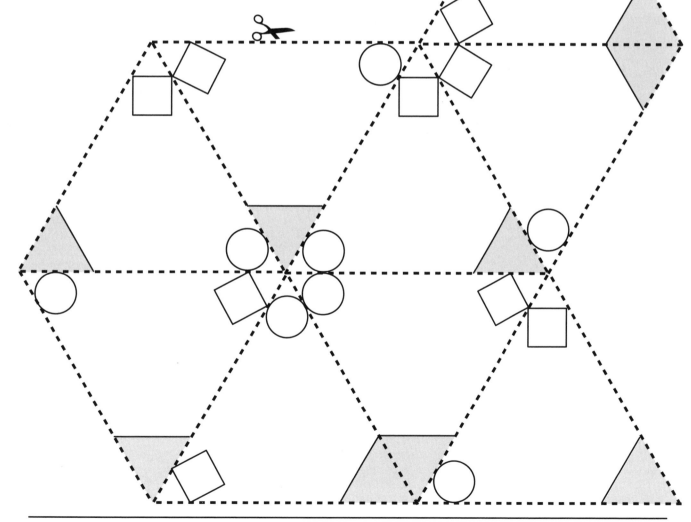

Name _____ Date _____

Estimating and Measuring Volume

1. Use 8 centimeter connecting cubes to make an object that will fit into a 250-cc graduated cylinder. What is the volume of your object?

   A. Fill a 250-cc graduated cylinder with a convenient amount of water. Good choices are 160 or 200 cc. Use an eyedropper to carefully add the last few drops.

   B. To read the water level correctly, put your eyes at the level of the water. When water creeps up the sides of a cylinder, it forms a **meniscus** which makes it look as though there are two lines. Read the lower line.

   C. Place your object made from connecting cubes into the cylinder. Slide it in gently so that no water will splash. Read the water level now.

   D. What is the difference in the level of the water before you added the object and after you added it? Explain the change in water level.

One way to find the volume of an object is to put the object underwater in a graduated cylinder and see how much the water rises. This is called finding **volume by displacement.** You are going to estimate the volume of objects using centimeter connecting cubes and find the volume of these objects by displacement.

2. Choose objects that will fit into a graduated cylinder. (Your teacher will help you.) Make a model of your objects using centimeter connecting cubes. Estimate the volume of the objects by counting the number of cubes in your models.

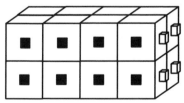

3. Find the volume of your objects by displacement.

4. Record your results in a table like the one below. Follow the examples.

Volume Data Table

Object	Estimated Volume from Cube Model	Volume by Displacement
Rock	11 cc	12 cc
Marker	14 cc	11 cc
Clay	16 cc	15 cc

5. Frank made a model of a marker using centimeter connecting cubes. By counting the cubes, he estimated that the marker has a volume of 14 cc. When he measured the volume using a graduated cylinder, he found the volume to be 11 cc. Why do you think there is a 3 cc difference?

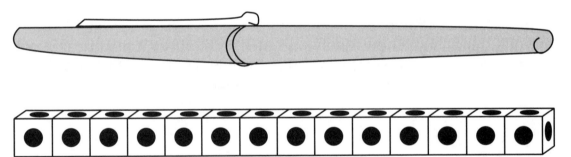

6. Were your estimates close to your measured volumes? Why or why not?

Homework

1. Look at the two scales on this page. How are they alike? How are they different?

2. How many cubic centimeters (cc) does each space represent on the scale for a 100-cc graduated cylinder?

3. How many cubic centimeters does each space represent on the scale for the 250-cc graduated cylinder?

4. Write the scale reading for each letter.

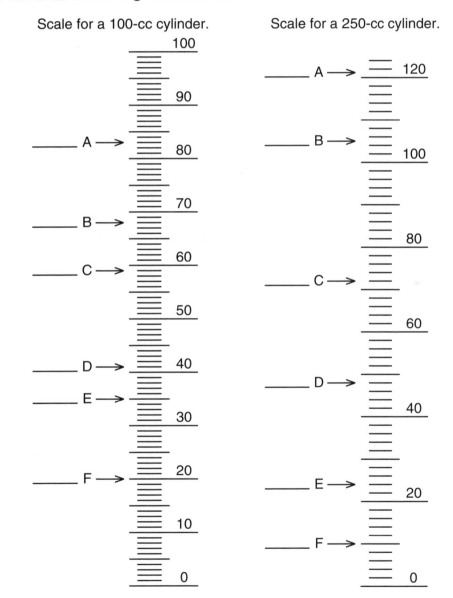

Scale for a 100-cc cylinder.   Scale for a 250-cc cylinder.

5. Shannon put a piece of clay under water in a graduated cylinder. What was the volume of the clay?

Name _____   Date _____

Mixed-Up Tables

Homework

Fill in these multiplication tables:

1.

×	2	4	8
2			
4		16	
8			

2.

×	1	3	9
1			
3			
9			

3. What patterns do you see in the table in Question 1?

4. What patterns do you see in the table in Question 2?

5.

×	10	5	0
10			
5			
0			

6.

×	6	5	7
6			
5			
7			

7. What patterns do you see in the table in Question 5?

8. What patterns do you see in the table in Question 6?

9.

×	8	6	4
8			
6			
4			

10.

×	8	6	3
8			
6			
3			

11.

×	2	5	8
9			
4			
7			

12.

×	7	6	4
3			
9			
10			

Fill in these division tables. Divide the large number across the top by the small number on the side.

13.

Dividend

÷	24	30	36
2			18
3		10	
6			

Divisor

14.

Dividend

÷	16	32	40
2			
4			
8			

Divisor

Spinner 1-4

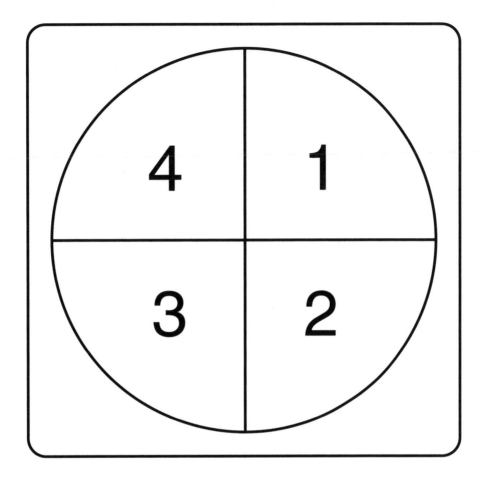

Predicting Prices

Homework

Look for patterns in each graph. If the points form a line, draw a best-fit line on the graph.

1.

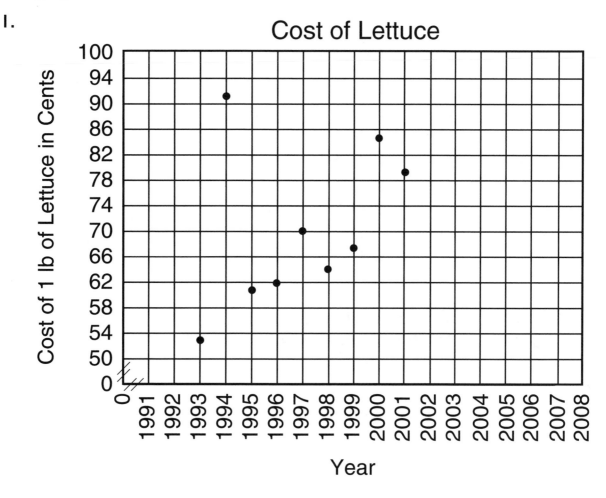

Cost of Lettuce

A. Using this data, can you make a reasonable prediction about the cost of lettuce in 2006? Why or why not?

B. If possible, predict the cost of one pound of lettuce in the year 2006.

C. Describe the graph. What do you think happened to the lettuce crop in 1994?

2.

Cost of Coffee

A. Using this data, can you make a reasonable prediction about the cost of a pound of ground coffee in the year 2008? Why or why not?

B. If possible, predict the cost of 1 pound of ground coffee in the year 2008.

3.

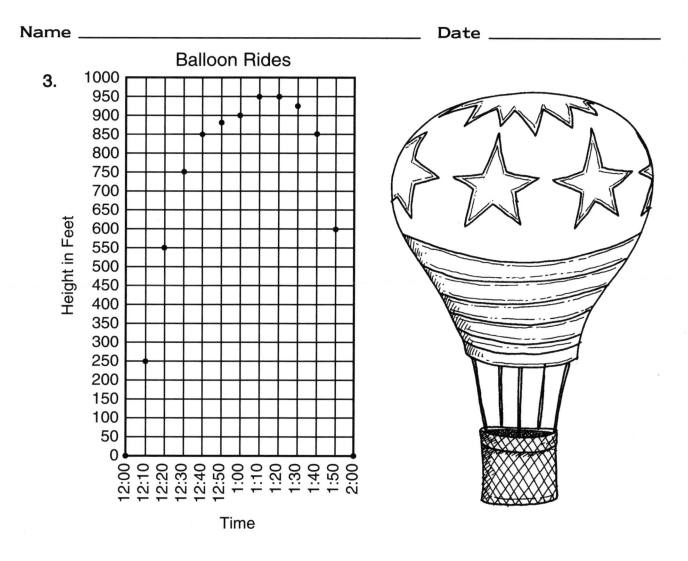

Balloon Rides

Height in Feet (y-axis, 0 to 1000 by 50)

Time (x-axis): 12:00, 12:10, 12:20, 12:30, 12:40, 12:50, 1:00, 1:10, 1:20, 1:30, 1:40, 1:50, 2:00

A. Using this data, can you make a reasonable prediction about the height of the balloon at 12:15? Why or why not?

B. If possible, predict the height of the balloon at 1:45.

C. Describe the graph. Why do you think the graph has the shape it does?

Experiment Review Chart

Directions:
- Write the names of the experiments completed this year in the first row of the table.
- Complete each column with information for each lab.

Name of Experiment → Experiment Elements ↓			
Main Variables			
Fixed Variables			
Anything Measured (units)			
Number of Trials			
Type of Graph			
Important Questions (Answers may vary.)			

Name_____ Date _____

Directions:
- Write the names of the experiments completed this year in the first row of the table.
- Complete each column with information for each lab.

Name of Experiment → / Experiment Elements ↓			
Main Variables			
Fixed Variables			
Anything Measured (units)			
Number of Trials			
Type of Graph			
Important Questions (Answers may vary.)			

Midyear Experiment and Portfolio Review

Triangle Flash Cards: 5s

- Work with a partner. Each partner cuts out the flash cards.
- To quiz you on a division fact, your partner covers the number in the square. Solve a division fact with the two uncovered numbers.
- Divide the used cards into three piles: those that you know and can answer quickly, those that you can figure out, and those that you need to learn.
- Practice the last two piles again. Then, make a list of the facts you need to practice at home.
- Go through the cards again. This time your partner covers the numbers in the circles.
- Sort the cards into the three piles. Make a list of the facts you need to practice at home.
- Repeat the directions for your partner.

Triangle Flash Cards: 1Os

- Work with a partner. Each partner cuts out the flash cards.
- To quiz you on a division fact, your partner covers the number in the square. Solve a division fact with the two uncovered numbers.
- Divide the used cards into three piles: those that you know and can answer quickly, those that you can figure out, and those that you need to learn.
- Practice the last two piles again. Then, make a list of the facts you need to practice at home.
- Go through the cards again. This time your partner covers the numbers in the circles.
- Sort the cards into the three piles. Make a list of the facts you need to practice at home.
- Repeat the directions for your partner.

Division Facts I Know

- Circle the facts you know well.
- Keep this table and use it to help you divide.
- As you learn more facts, you may circle them too.

×	0	1	2	3	4	5	6	7	8	9	10
0	0	0	0	0	0	0	0	0	0	0	0
1	0	1	2	3	4	5	6	7	8	9	10
2	0	2	4	6	8	10	12	14	16	18	20
3	0	3	6	9	12	15	18	21	24	27	30
4	0	4	8	12	16	20	24	28	32	36	40
5	0	5	10	15	20	25	30	35	40	45	50
6	0	6	12	18	24	30	36	42	48	54	60
7	0	7	14	21	28	35	42	49	56	63	70
8	0	8	16	24	32	40	48	56	64	72	80
9	0	9	18	27	36	45	54	63	72	81	90
10	0	10	20	30	40	50	60	70	80	90	100

Divisor

Unit 9

SHAPES AND SOLIDS

	Student Guide	Discovery Assignment Book	Adventure Book	Unit Resource Guide*
Lesson 1				
Lines	◉			
Lesson 2				
What's Your Angle?	◉	◉		
Lesson 3				
Symmetry	◉	◉		
Lesson 4				
Journey to Flatopia			◉	
Lesson 5				
Prisms	◉	◉		
Lesson 6				
Finding the Volume of a Prism	◉			
Lesson 7				
Building an Octahedron		◉		
Lesson 8				
Constructing a Prism				◉

Unit Resource Guide pages are from the teacher materials.

Unit 9: Home Practice

Part 1 Triangle Flash Cards: 5s and 10s

Study for the quiz on the division facts for the 5s and 10s. Take home your *Triangle Flash Cards* and your list of facts you need to study.

Here's how to use the flash cards. Ask a family member to choose one flash card at a time. Your partner should cover one of the smaller numbers. (One of the smaller numbers is in a circle. The other number is in a square.) Solve a division fact using the two uncovered numbers. Go through the cards a second time, this time cover the other small number.

Your teacher will tell you when the quiz on the 5s and 10s will be. Remember to concentrate on one small group of facts each night—about 8 to 10 facts. Also, remember to concentrate on those facts you cannot answer correctly and quickly.

Part 2 Mental Multiplication

1. Use mental math to solve Questions 1A–1F.

   A. $6000 \times 10 =$ _____

   B. $500 \times 70 =$ _____

   C. $60 \times 60 =$ _____

   D. $9000 \times 5 =$ _____

   E. $100 \times 800 =$ _____

   F. $500 \times 50 =$ _____

2. A. Paper towels cost 80¢. How much will 6 rolls cost?

   B. One ice cream bar costs $3.50. How much will 4 bars cost?

   C. Bagels cost 69¢ each. About how much will 5 bagels cost?

3. How much is:
   A. 13 nickels?

   B. 11 nickels and 5 dimes?

   C. 5 quarters and 17 nickels?

Part 3 Addition, Subtraction, and Multiplication

1. Find the missing numbers needed to make these addition and subtraction problems correct. Use pencil and paper only.

A.
```
  189
+ ___
  612
```

B.
```
  322
- ___
  284
```

C.
```
  5078
+ ___
  8079
```

D.
```
  7339
- ___
  6079
```

E.
```
    5405
+   ___
  13,053
```

F.
```
  3000
- ___
  1456
```

2. Estimate the following products using convenient numbers. Write a number sentence to show your thinking.

A. $290 \times 18 =$

B. $505 \times 59 =$

C. $9956 \times 9 =$

3. Find the products using paper and pencil or mental math. Be sure to estimate to make sure your answers are reasonable.

A. $63 \times 4 =$

B. $37 \times 8 =$

C. $28 \times 9 =$

D. $84 \times 4 =$

E. $66 \times 3 =$

F. $72 \times 6 =$

Part 4 Time

1. What time is shown on each clock below?

A.   **B.**   **C.**

D.   **E.**   **F.**

2. **A.** Jackie began cleaning her room at 6:15 P.M. If it took Jackie two hours to clean her room, at what time did she finish?

    B. John started watching cartoons when he woke up 1 hour and 15 minutes ago. It is now 10:00 A.M. What time did John wake up?

    C. Jacob's mother has to pick him up from his aunt's house at 9:30 P.M. It takes 50 minutes to get there. What time should she leave her home?

    D. Irma and her sister are making dinner for the family. They plan to eat at 6:30 P.M. The dinner takes 2 hours and 35 minutes to prepare. What time should they begin cooking?

    E. How many minutes will it take Irma and her sister to prepare dinner?

    F. How many hours is 600 minutes?

Part 5 Geometry

You will need a protractor, a ruler, and two pieces of *Centimeter Grid Paper* to complete this part of the Home Practice.

1. Nicholas built the prism at the right from centimeter connecting cubes.

   A. How many centimeters tall is the prism?

   B. How many square centimeters cover the base of the prism?

   C. What is the volume of the prism?

2. What is the volume of each of the prisms below? Show how you found your answer.

   A.   **B.** The area of the base is 56 sq cm.

   3 cm

   7 cm

   7 cm

   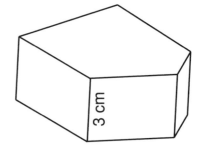

   3 cm

3. Draw each of the angles described below with a ruler and protractor on a separate sheet of paper.

   A. Draw a 35° angle. Name the angle ∠QRT.

   B. Draw a 142° angle. Name the angle ∠XYZ.

4. Go to a cupboard (ask an adult first). Select three objects that are prisms (boxes) such as a gelatin box, a small cereal box, and a toothpaste box.

   A. Estimate the volume in cubic centimeters of each box.

   B. Trace the base of each on *Centimeter Grid Paper*. How many sq cm cover the base of each box?

   C. Measure the height of each box in cm.

   D. Use the information you gathered in 4B and 4C to find the volume of each container. Were your estimates close to your answers?

Measuring Angles I

Measure each of the angles in Questions 1–6 with your protractor. To measure, you may need to extend the sides of some of the angles with the edge of your protractor. Label each angle as acute, obtuse, or right.

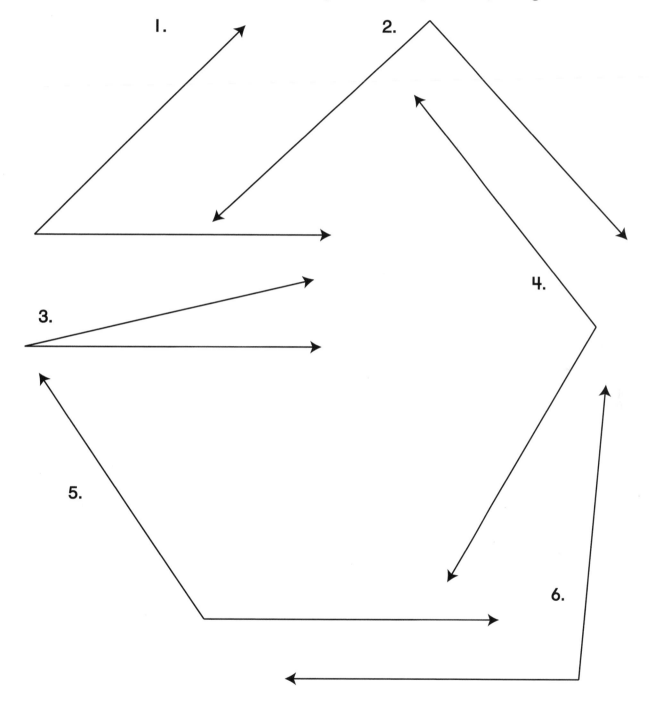

Name _____ Date _____

Pattern Block Shapes

Cut out the shapes below. Answer the following questions for each. Does the shape have line symmetry? If the shape has line symmetry, how many lines of symmetry does it have? Draw in the lines of symmetry.

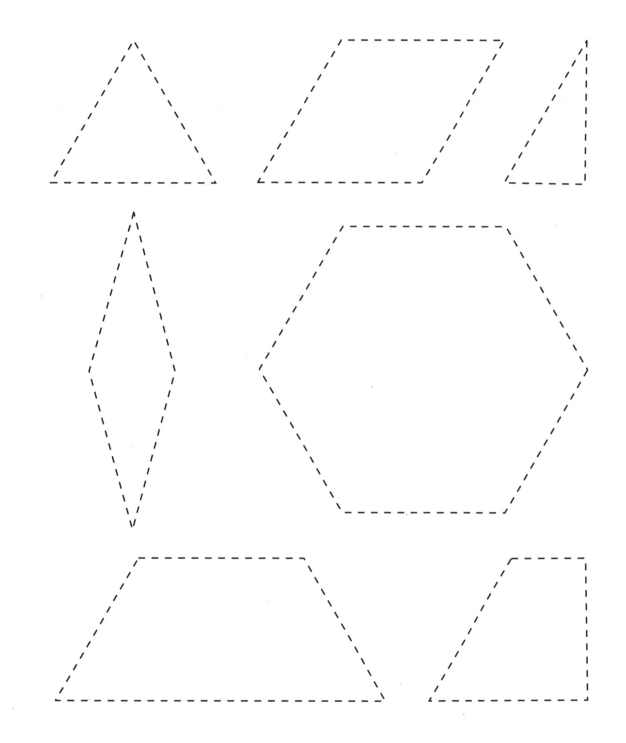

Symmetry

Line Symmetry Examples

Each of the pictures here has line symmetry.

- **Cut out each shape.**

- **Fold the shapes to find the line(s) of symmetry. Remember, if you fold the shape along a line of symmetry, the two pieces will fit exactly on top of one another.**

- **Draw a line(s) of symmetry on each shape.**

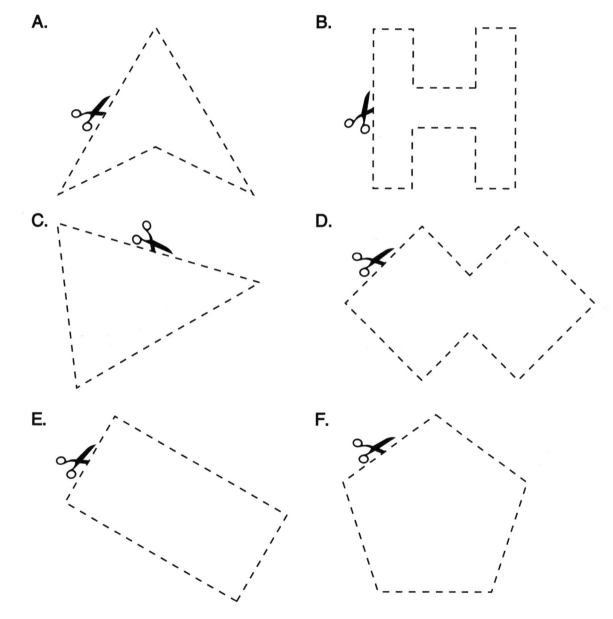

A.

B.

C.

D.

E.

F.

Turn Symmetry Examples

The pictures here all have turn symmetry. The center of turning is marked on each.

- **Cut out each of the shapes on the bottom half of this page.**

- **Place each cutout on top of its template below. Place your pencil point directly on the center of turning. As you turn the cutout 360° (a full turn), how many times do the two pictures match after turning?**

- **Find the type of turn symmetry for each picture. Label each one.**

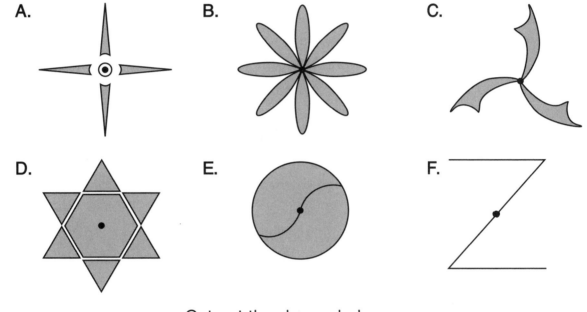

A.   B.   C.

D.   E.   F.

------------------------------ Cut out the shapes below. ------------------------------

Blank Spinners

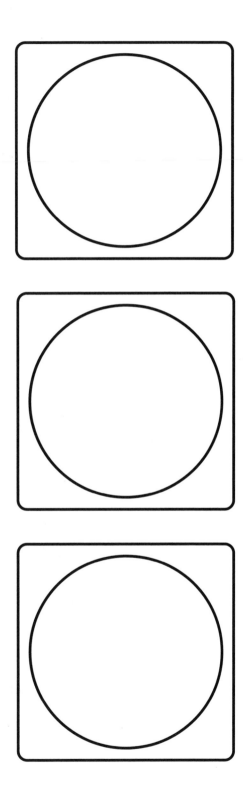

More Symmetry

Homework

1. Parts of the pictures below are missing. The lines are lines of symmetry. Draw in the missing parts.

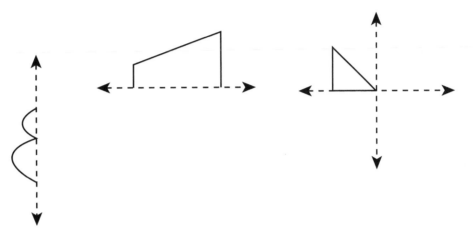

2. Which of the pictures below have turn symmetry? What kind of turn symmetry? (*Hint:* Trace the shapes and cut out the tracings. Then, place the tracing on top of the picture and turn it.)

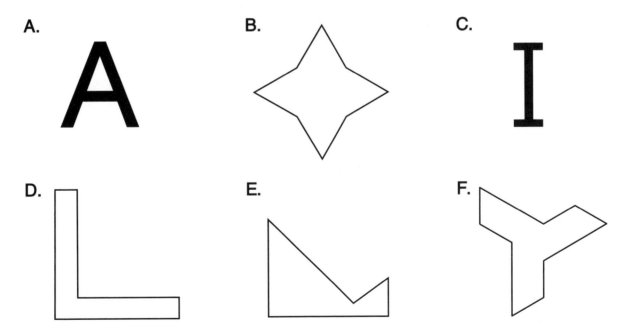

A.

B.

C.

D.

E.

F.

3. Which of the pictures in Question 2 have line symmetry? Draw in the line(s) of symmetry. (*Hint:* You may cut out the shapes and fold them.)

5.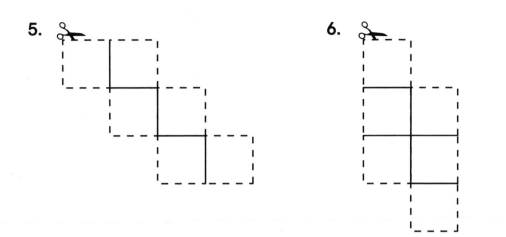

6.

A Hexagonal Prism

You will need a protractor, ruler, scissors, and tape to complete the activity. Answer Questions 1–6 before cutting out the net of the hexagonal prism.

Look at the net on the following page. It contains two hexagons. **Hexagons** are polygons with six sides.

1. What is the measure of the angles of the hexagons?

2. What is the length of the sides of the hexagons in centimeters?

3. What are the lengths of the sides of the rectangles in centimeters (to the nearest centimeter)?

4. What point on the rectangle will point E touch when the net is cut and folded?

5. What point on the rectangle will point D touch when the net is cut and folded?

6. What point on the rectangle will point B touch when the net is cut and folded?

Carefully cut the net. If you are using heavier paper, score the inside lines. To score means to use a ruler and sharp pencil to trace the lines you are going to fold. It will make the folds much neater. Then, fold and tape.

You may wish to decorate the net before cutting and folding. Think about which side will be on the inside and which side will show on the outside.

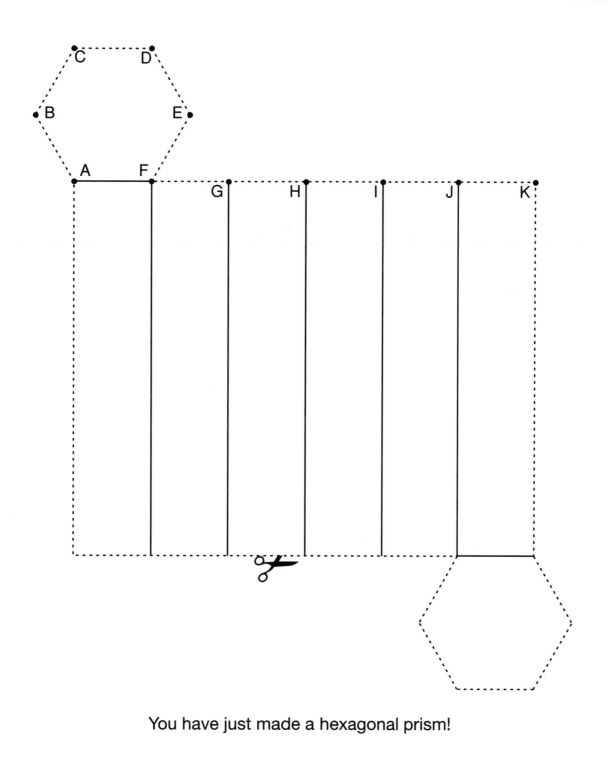

You have just made a hexagonal prism!

Right Triangular Prism

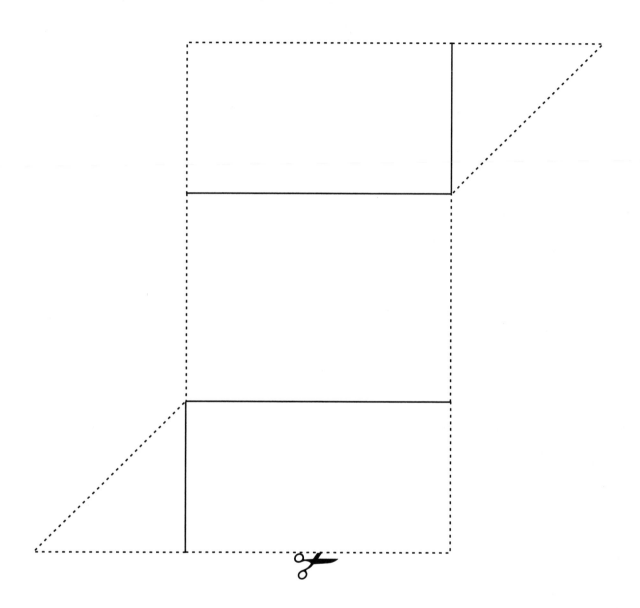

Net of an Octahedron

Unit 10

Using Decimals

	Student Guide	Discovery Assignment Book	Adventure Book	Unit Resource Guide*
Lesson 1 m, dm, cm, mm	⊙	⊙		
Lesson 2 Tenths	⊙	⊙		
Lesson 3 Hundredths	⊙	⊙		⊙
Lesson 4 Downhill Racer	⊙			⊙
Lesson 5 Decimal Hex		⊙		
Lesson 6 Alberto in TenthsLand			⊙	

Unit Resource Guide pages are from the teacher materials.

Unit 10: Home Practice

Part 1 Triangle Flash Cards: 2s and 3s

Study for the quiz on the division facts for the 2s and 3s. Take home your *Triangle Flash Cards* and your list of facts you need to study.

Here's how to use the flash cards. Ask a family member to choose one flash card at a time. Your partner should cover the corner containing either the square or the circle. This number will be the answer to a division fact. Solve a division problem with the two uncovered numbers.

Your teacher will tell you when the quiz on the 2s and 3s will be. Remember to concentrate on one small group of facts each night—about 8 to 10 facts. Also, remember to study only those facts you cannot answer correctly and quickly.

Part 2 Missing Numbers and Big Numbers

1. What number must *n* be to make each number sentence true? After you have decided on a number for *n*, check your work by multiplying.

   A. $n \times 20 = 80$ B. $300 \times n = 1800$ C. $90 \times n = 2700$

   D. $50 \times n = 10,000$ E. $n \times 50 = 1500$ F. $70 \times n = 210$

2. A. Write the following numbers in order from smallest to largest.

   45,676   54,673   45,788   48,654   47,998   45,089

   B. Round 48,654 to the nearest thousand.

   C. Round 45,089 to the nearest hundred.

3. Use convenient numbers to estimate the answers to the following problems. Record number sentences to show your thinking.

   A. $608,965 + 28,696$ B. $2,657,223 + 3,908,700$ C. $378,904 - 99,645$

Name_____ Date _____

Part 3 Decimals

1. Numbers are represented in base-ten shorthand below. The flat is one whole. Label each of the following with its correct number. Then, put the numbers in order from least to greatest.

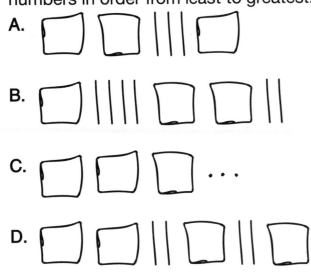

A.

B.

C.

D.

2. Write a decimal for each of the following. Then, show your decimal using base-ten shorthand. The flat is one whole. Find a number that is:

   A. Between 8 and 9

   B. Between 4 and 4.5

   C. Just a little bigger than 8

   D. Between $\frac{1}{2}$ and 2

3. For each of the two problems below, put the measurements in order from shortest to longest.

   A. 0.6 m   23 cm   1 dm   0.45 m   55 dm

   B. 1.5 m   1 m and 8 dm   1.03 meter   1.24 meter

USING DECIMALS

Part 4 School Supplies

Linda and her brother are buying school supplies. Notebooks are on sale for 39¢ each. Pencils are 4 for $1.00. A set of markers costs $2.98. Folders are 10 for $1.00.

1. Linda needs 3 notebooks, 1 set of markers, 1 folder, and 8 pencils. Estimate the cost of Linda's school supplies. Use number sentences to show your thinking.

2. Linda's brother needs 5 notebooks, 1 set of markers, 3 folders, and 4 pencils. Estimate the cost of his school supplies. Use number sentences to show your thinking.

3. What is the exact cost of each child's supplies? (There is no tax.)

4. What is the difference in price between the two children's supplies? Use a number sentence to show how you solved the problem.

Part 5 Addition, Subtraction, and Multiplication

Solve the following problems using paper and pencil or mental math. Estimate to make sure your answers are reasonable.

1. **A.** $68 - 49 =$ **B.** $167 + 67 =$ **C.** $284 + 238 =$ **D.** $432 - 197 =$

    E. $47 \times 9 =$ **F.** $26 \times 7 =$ **G.** $34 \times 9 =$ **H.** $23 \times 8 =$

2. Explain your estimation strategy for Question 1F.

3. Explain a possible mental math strategy for Question 1D.

Part 6 Playing at the Park

1. **A.** When Shannon and her family arrived at the park on Saturday, Shannon counted 3 children on *each* of the following: the slide, the swings, the monkey bars, and the merry-go-round. How many children were at the park when Shannon arrived?

   B. If there were 8 more children than adults at the park, how many adults were at the park?

2. A used car dealer is across the street from the park. Shannon's dad looked at some cars while Shannon and her sister played at the park. He liked two different cars. One car costs $4550 and the other costs $3775. What is the difference in price of the two cars?

3. Shannon treated her little sister and her mother to a treat. At a nearby stand she bought two cans of juice at 65¢ each and three popsicles at 85¢ each. She gave the vendor $5.00. How much change will Shannon receive?

4. While playing in the park, Shannon's family saw a 5 kilometer race. 235 people were signed up to participate, but only 178 arrived the day of the race. How many people did not show up for the race?

5. **A.** Last summer, the park district raised money for new playground equipment. In June, $565 was raised. In July, $438 was raised. In August, $395 was raised. How much money was raised for new playground equipment?

   B. How much money do they need to raise in September to reach their goal of $1500?

Triangle Flash Cards: 2s

- Work with a partner. Each partner cuts out the flash cards.
- To quiz you on a division fact, your partner covers the number in the square. Solve a division fact with the two uncovered numbers.
- Divide the used cards into three piles: those that you know and can answer quickly, those that you can figure out, and those that you need to learn.
- Practice the last two piles again. Then, make a list of the facts you need to practice at home.
- Go through the cards again. This time your partner covers the numbers in the circles.
- Sort the cards into the three piles. Make a list of the facts you need to practice at home.
- Repeat the directions for your partner.

Triangle Flash Cards: 3s

- Work with a partner. Each partner cuts out the flash cards.
- To quiz you on a division fact, your partner covers the number in the square. Solve a division fact with the two uncovered numbers.
- Divide the used cards into three piles: those that you know and can answer quickly, those that you can figure out, and those that you need to learn.
- Practice the last two piles again. Then, make a list of the facts you need to practice at home.
- Go through the cards again. This time your partner covers the numbers in the circles.
- Sort the cards into the three piles. Make a list of the facts you need to practice at home.
- Repeat the directions for your partner.

Measure Hunt

Find four lengths in the classroom using the rules in the table below. Use the fewest pieces possible when you measure. Use metersticks to measure meters. Use skinnies to measure decimeters. Use bits to measure centimeters. Then, complete the table. An example is done for you.

Table 1

Rule	Object	Number of			Length (nearest 0.01 m)
		m	dm	cm	
Between 1 and 2 m	Height of cabinet	1	2	0	1.20
Between 1 and 1.5 m					
Between 0.5 and 1 m					
Between 0.5 and 0.8 m					
Between 0.55 and 0.75 m					

Find five lengths in the classroom using the rules in the table below. Use metersticks to measure the lengths. Then, complete the table.

Table 2

Rule	Object	Number of			Length (nearest 0.01 m)
		m	dm	cm	
Between 1 and 2 m					
Between 1 and 1.5 m					
Between 0.5 and 1 m					
Between 0.6 and 0.9 m					
Between 0.40 and 0.65 m					

m, dm, cm, mm

Exploring Tenths

Use base-ten shorthand to help you answer the following questions.

1. Michael placed 14 skinnies on his *Tenths Helper* chart. Write the number this represents in more than one way.

2. A. Grace wanted to build the number 1.9 on her *Tenths Helper* chart using skinnies. How many skinnies will she need to build this number?

   B. Grace decided to use both flats and skinnies to build this number. How many flats will she need? How many skinnies?

3. Nila built the following number on her *Tenths Helper* chart:

   Write this number in more than one way.

4. A. Jackie placed 4 flats on her desk. How many whole units does this represent?

   B. She added 6 skinnies to the 4 flats. What number does 4 flats and 6 skinnies represent?

5. A. Jacob placed 6 skinnies along the edge of a meterstick. The length of 6 skinnies is what fraction of a meter?

   B. Write this fraction as both a decimal fraction and a common fraction.

6. A. Jessie measured the length of a table in her classroom using skinnies. She found the length of the table was 18 skinnies. How many whole meters and how many more tenths does this represent?

   B. Write the length of the table in more than one way.

7. Use what you know about tenths to complete the table by filling in the missing information. (Remember: A flat is one whole.)

Base-Ten Shorthand	Common Fraction	Decimal Fraction
///// ////	$\frac{9}{10}$	
		6.7
▢▢▢▢▢▢////		
	$23\frac{6}{10}$	
		52.3
▢▢▢▢///// //		
▢▢▢▢▢ //		
	$34\frac{5}{10}$	
▢▢▢▢▢▢///		

Grace's Base-Ten Pieces

Use base-ten pieces (packs, flats, and skinnies only). A flat is one whole.

1. If a flat is 1, then what number is a pack?

2. If a flat is 1, then what number is a skinny?

Grace has two base-ten pieces. She might have skinnies, flats, or packs. For example, she might have a skinny and a flat. She might have something else.

3. Find all possible sets of pieces that Grace might have. Use base-ten shorthand to show each set she might have. Write a number for each set.

4. What is the largest number that Grace could possibly have?

5. What is the smallest number that Grace could possibly have?

6. Put the numbers that Grace could have in order from smallest to largest.

Hundredths, Hundredths, Hundredths

This is a game for two people. You need base-ten pieces (flats, skinnies, and bits). Use the *Shorthand and Fractions Table* to record your work. For this game, a flat is one whole.

Shorthand and Fractions Table

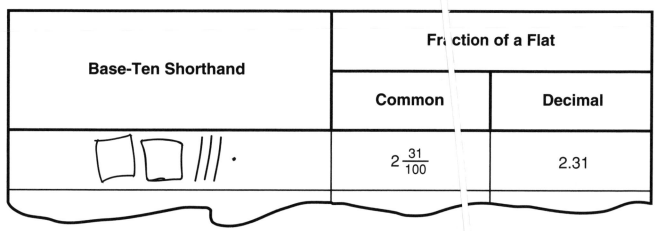

Base-Ten Shorthand	Fraction of a Flat	
	Common	**Decimal**
	$2\frac{31}{100}$	2.31

To play, the first player makes a number with base-ten pieces and shows it in the table using base-ten shorthand.

Then, the second player must write the fractions for the number and say the number.

The second player scores one point for writing the common fraction correctly, one point for writing the decimal fraction correctly, and one point for saying the number correctly.

Take turns making, writing, and saying numbers.

In this game, you are allowed to be tricky. Can you tell what this number is?

Shorthand and Fractions Table

You need base-ten pieces. For this page, a flat is one whole.

Base-Ten Shorthand	Fraction of a Flat	
	Common	Decimal

Decimal Hex

This is a game for two or three players.

Materials

- *Decimal Hex* Game Board on the following page
- two same color centimeter cubes or other game markers for each player
- one clear plastic spinner or pencil and paper clip

Rules

The goal of this game is to move two cubes or other markers from matching hexagons to opposite matching hexagons that all have the same number.

I. Each player places both of his or her cubes on two matching hexagons with the same number. The target hexagons are the matching ones with the same number on the other side of the game board.

2. The first player spins the spinner.

3. If "Greater Than or Equal To" shows, the player can move one cube to a neighboring hexagon with a number that is greater than or equal to the number in the hexagon where the cube is now.

4. If "Less Than or Equal To" shows, the player can move one cube to a neighboring hexagon with a number that is less than or equal to the number in the hexagon where the cube is now.

5. The player does not have to move a cube during his or her turn.

6. More than one cube can be on the same hexagon at the same time.

7. Players take turns spinning the spinner and moving cubes.

8. The first player to get both cubes to his or her target hexagons is the winner.

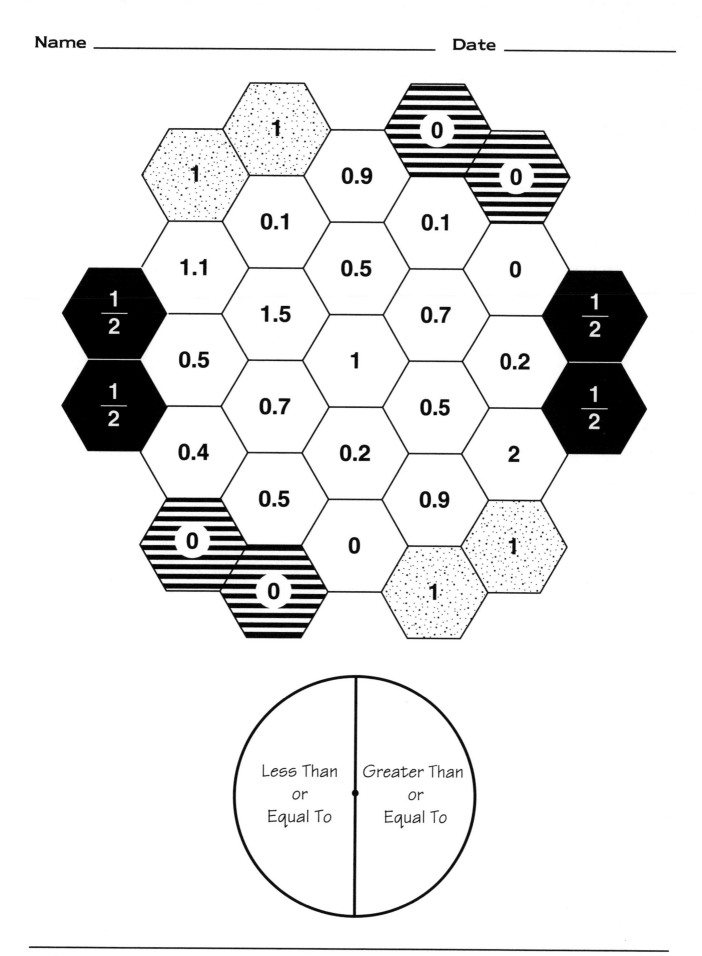

Unit 11
MULTIPLICATION

	Student Guide	Discovery Assignment Book	Adventure Book	Unit Resource Guide*
Lesson 1				
Modeling Multiplication	◎			
Lesson 2				
More Multiplication	◎			
Lesson 3				
Compact Multiplication	◎			
Lesson 4				
All-Partials Revisited	◎			◎
Lesson 5				
More Compact Multiplication	◎			
Lesson 6				
Phil and Howard's Excellent Egyptian Adventure			◎	
Lesson 7				
Visiting Egypt	◎			

Unit Resource Guide pages are from the teacher materials.

Unit 11: Home Practice

Part 1 Triangle Flash Cards: Square Numbers

Study for the quiz on the division facts for the square numbers. Take home your *Triangle Flash Cards* and your list of facts you need to study.

Here's how to use the flash cards. Ask a family member to choose one flash card at a time. Your partner should cover one of the two small numbers. This number will be the answer to a division fact. Solve a division problem with the two uncovered numbers.

Your teacher will tell you when you will have a quiz on the division facts for the square numbers. Remember to study only those facts you cannot answer correctly and quickly.

Part 2 Big Numbers

1. Write the following numbers:

   A. six hundred thirty thousand _____

   B. one million, four hundred ten thousand, nineteen _____

2. Write the following in words:

   A. 420,079 _____

   _____

   B. 6,122,038 _____

   _____

3. Choose from the following numbers to answer Questions 3A and 3B.

   46,998   56,888   45,788   48,998   45,088

   A. If you add 2 to one of the numbers, you will get 49,000. Which number?

   _____

   B. If you add 11,100 to one of the numbers, you will get 58,098. Which number?

   _____

Part 3 Multiples of 10 and 100

Do the following problems in your head. Write only the answers.

A. $9 \times 30 =$ _____ **B.** $20 \times 30 =$ _____ **C.** $20 \times 20 =$ _____

D. $900 \times 300 =$ _____ **E.** $60 \times 60 =$ _____ **F.** $40 \times 400 =$ _____

G. $70 \times 700 =$ _____ **H.** $30 \times 800 =$ _____ **I.** $5 \times 30 =$ _____

Part 4 Writing Numbers

For each of the following numbers, write two other numbers: one that is a little smaller and one that is a little larger. You may use a number line to help you.

	A Little Smaller	A Little Larger
A. one million	_____	_____
B. one-half million	_____	_____
C. ten million	_____	_____
D. 1,300,000	_____	_____
E. 999,999	_____	_____
F. five thousand	_____	_____

Part 5 Addition and Subtraction Practice

Use paper and pencil or mental math only. Estimate to see if your answers are reasonable.

A. $\begin{array}{r} 92 \\ + 65 \\ \hline \end{array}$ **B.** $\begin{array}{r} 340 \\ - 235 \\ \hline \end{array}$ **C.** $\begin{array}{r} 58 \\ - 49 \\ \hline \end{array}$

D. $\begin{array}{r} 5001 \\ - 999 \\ \hline \end{array}$ **E.** $\begin{array}{r} 1490 \\ + 453 \\ \hline \end{array}$ **F.** $\begin{array}{r} 289 \\ + 39 \\ \hline \end{array}$

G. Choose one problem and explain a strategy for solving it using mental math.

Part 6 More Multiples of 10 and 100

Use only paper and pencil or mental math to solve the following problems. Show your work on a separate sheet of paper. Estimate to see if your answers are reasonable. Be prepared to explain your estimates.

1. **A.** $25 \times 20 =$ **B.** $31 \times 40 =$ **C.** $96 \times 30 =$

   D. $92 \times 300 =$ **E.** $68 \times 200 =$ **F.** $47 \times 90 =$

   G. $340 \times 9 =$ **H.** $450 \times 4 =$ **I.** $2900 \times 4 =$

2. Explain your strategy for estimating the product in Question 1C.

Part 7 Multiplication Practice

Use only paper and pencil or mental math to solve the following problems. Show your work on a separate piece of paper. Be prepared to explain how you estimated to see if your answers were reasonable.

1. **A.** $450 \times 3 =$ **B.** $454 \times 9 =$

   C. $2090 \times 6 =$ **D.** $90 \times 13 =$

   E. $95 \times 20 =$ **F.** $82 \times 30 =$

   G. $63 \times 22 =$ **H.** $75 \times 75 =$

   I. $129 \times 7 =$ **J.** $432 \times 6 =$

2. Explain your strategy for estimating the product in Question 1B.

Part 8 Metric Measurement

Use kilometers, meters, decimeters, centimeters, and millimeters to label these distances.

A. The height of a room is about 3 _____.

B. The length of a sofa is about 20 _____.

C. The width of a sharp pencil point is about 2 _____.

D. The length of a pencil is about 14 _____.

E. The distance from Chicago to Dallas is about 1500 _____.

Part 9 Money

Luis has 3 dimes, 3 nickels, and 3 quarters. Help him find all the possible amounts he can make using 3 of his coins. Show how you organized your work.

Part 10 The Shortcut

Decide if the following are divisible without actually dividing them out. Explain your strategy.

A. Is 5367 divisible by 2?

B. Is 546,890 divisible by 10?

C. Is 11,952 divisible by 6, 3, and 2?

D. Is 74,981 divisible by 9?

E. Is 431,895 divisible by 5 and 10?

F. Give a three-digit number that is divisible by 9.

G. Give a four-digit number that is divisible by 5.

Part 11 Shortcuts for Checking Answers

Use what you know about divisibility rules to check the answers to these problems. If you find an incorrect answer, solve the problem and write the correct answer. Use a separate sheet of paper if you need more room to show your work.

A.   156
    × 9

   1404

B.   562
    × 9

   5008

C.   231
    × 6

   386

D.   410
    × 6

   2460

E.   1490
    × 3

   4470

F.   289
    × 2

   577

Triangle Flash Cards: Square Numbers

- Work with a partner. Each partner cuts out the flash cards.
- To quiz you on a division fact, your partner covers one of the numbers in the unshaded corners. Solve a division fact with the two uncovered numbers.
- Divide the used cards into three piles: those that you know and can answer quickly, those that you can figure out, and those that you need to learn.
- Practice the last two piles again. Then, make a list of the facts you need to practice at home.
- Repeat the directions for your partner.

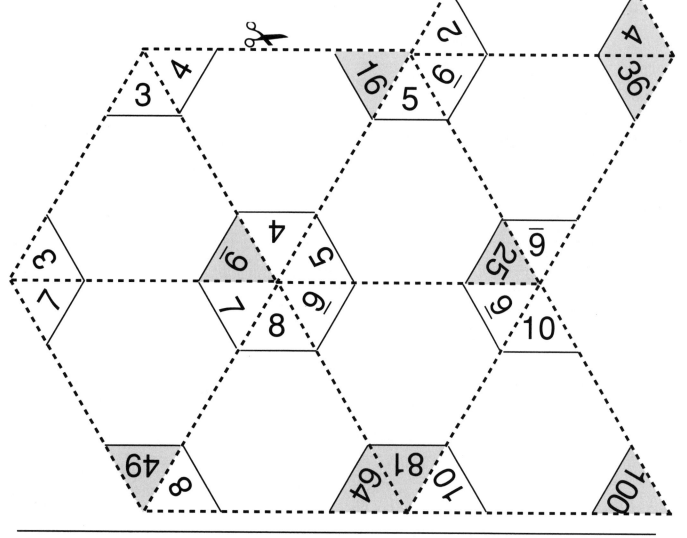

Unit 12
Exploring Fractions

	Student Guide	Discovery Assignment Book	Adventure Book	Unit Resource Guide*
Lesson 1				
Fraction Strips	◎	◎		
Lesson 2				
Adding and Subtracting with Fraction Strips	◎			
Lesson 3				
Comparing Fractions	◎			
Lesson 4				
Frabble Game and Bubble Sort	◎	◎		
Lesson 5				
Equivalent Fractions	◎			
Lesson 6				
Pattern Block Fractions	◎			◎
Lesson 7				
Solving Problems with Pattern Blocks	◎			
Lesson 8				
Fraction Puzzles	◎			◎
Lesson 9				
Midterm Test				◎

Unit Resource Guide pages are from the teacher materials.

Unit 12: Home Practice

Part 1 Triangle Flash Cards: 9s

Study for the quiz on the division facts for the nines. Take home your *Triangle Flash Cards: 9s* and your list of facts you need to study.

Ask a family member to choose one flash card at a time. He or she should cover one of the smaller numbers. (One of the smaller numbers is circled. The other has a square around it.) Solve a division fact using the two uncovered numbers. Ask your family member to sometimes cover the circled numbers and sometimes cover the number in the square.

Your teacher will tell you when the quiz on the nines will be.

Part 2 Multiplication

1. Solve the following problems in your head. Remember to follow the proper order of operations.

   A. $87 \times 0 =$ _____

   B. $211 \times 1 =$ _____

   C. $0 \times 1800 =$ _____

   D. $1 \times 7898 =$ _____

   E. $8 \times 0 + 8 =$ _____

   F. $7 + 1 \times 10 =$ _____

   G. $16 \times 1 - 7 =$ _____

   H. $6 \times 1 - 2 \times 0 =$ _____

   I. $20 - 0 \times 7 =$ _____

   J. $20 \times 7 - 0 =$ _____

2. Explain why all the multiples of 6 are even numbers. First, write all the multiples of 6 in order from 6 to 60.

Name _____ Date _____

Part 3 Fraction Chart

Use the fraction chart you created in Lesson 3 or the Fraction Chart in your *Student Guide* in Lesson 3.

1. Order these fractions from smallest to largest.

   A. $\frac{2}{3}$ $\frac{1}{4}$ $\frac{5}{6}$ $\frac{3}{8}$ $\frac{2}{12}$ _____

   B. $\frac{3}{5}$ $\frac{1}{8}$ $\frac{4}{9}$ $\frac{1}{10}$ $\frac{1}{2}$ _____

2. Find one or two equivalent fractions for each of the following.

   A. $\frac{6}{8}$ B. $\frac{3}{9}$ C. $\frac{2}{3}$ D. $\frac{4}{10}$

   E. $\frac{3}{5}$ F. $\frac{3}{12}$ G. $\frac{6}{12}$ H. $\frac{1}{5}$

3. Complete the number sentences.

   A. $\frac{5}{6} = \frac{?}{12}$ B. $\frac{8}{10} = \frac{4}{?}$ C. $\frac{4}{5} = \frac{?}{20}$

4. Name a fraction smaller than each of the following.

   A. $\frac{1}{2}$ B. $\frac{1}{4}$ C. $\frac{3}{5}$ D. $\frac{7}{8}$

5. Name a fraction greater than each of the following. Do not name a fraction equivalent to 1.

   A. $\frac{1}{2}$ B. $\frac{3}{4}$ C. $\frac{1}{6}$ D. $\frac{9}{10}$

EXPLORING FRACTIONS

Part 4 Fractions and Decimals

Complete this table. The flat equals one whole.

Base-Ten Shorthand	Common Fraction	Decimal Fraction
$\|/$	$\frac{25}{100}$ or $\frac{1}{4}$	0.25
☐·		
		0.03
☐☐☐☐☐ /|/||		
	$\frac{3}{10}$	
		4.37
☐☐		
	$4\frac{16}{100}$	
		10.41

Part 5 A Fraction of a Meter

Use your fraction chart from Lesson 3, the Fraction Chart in your *Student Guide,* or a meterstick to help you compare fractions.

1. Name a measurement that is greater than $\frac{1}{2}$ meter but less than $\frac{7}{10}$ of a meter.

2. Which is longer: $\frac{7}{10}$ of a meter or 50 centimeters?

3. Name a measurement that is a little less than $\frac{3}{10}$ of a meter.

4. Name a fraction of a meter that is longer than $\frac{5}{100}$ of a meter and shorter than 0.2 meter.

5. Name a fraction that is less than $\frac{7}{10}$ but more than $\frac{1}{5}$.

6. Name a measurement that is longer than 1.54 meters but shorter than $1\frac{9}{10}$ meters.

7. Name a measurement that is more than three times as long as $\frac{1}{2}$ of a meter.

Part 6 Arithmetic Review

1. Solve the following problems using mental math or paper and pencil. Estimate to make sure your answers are reasonable.

   A. $231 \times 4 =$ **B.** $409 \times 5 =$ **C.** $6283 \times 4 =$ **D.** $570 \times 5 =$

   E. $46 \times 92 =$ **F.** $27 \times 44 =$ **G.** $70 \times 40 =$ **H.** $83 \times 50 =$

   I. $1092 + 378 =$ **J.** $3807 - 797 =$ **K.** $3450 + 4750 =$ **L.** $8367 - 538 =$

2. Explain your estimation strategy for Question 1C.

3. Solve the following problems.

   A. John's uncle is taking a test to be a cashier at a grocery store. He must show all the ways to give 59¢ in change using exactly 10 coins. Show at least two ways to do this.

   B. The questions on a math test are each worth a certain number of points. Use the table to find the total points if the four questions are answered correctly.

Question	Points Possible
A	$2\frac{1}{2}$
B	$3\frac{1}{4}$
C	5
D	$4\frac{1}{4}$

Triangle Flash Cards: 9s

- Work with a partner. Each partner cuts out the flash cards.
- To quiz you on a division fact, your partner covers the number in the square. Solve a division fact with the two uncovered numbers.
- Divide the used cards into three piles: those that you know and can answer quickly, those that you can figure out, and those that you need to learn.
- Practice the last two piles again. Then, make a list of the facts you need to practice at home.
- Go through the cards again. This time your partner covers the numbers in the circles.
- Sort the cards into the three piles. Make a list of the facts you need to practice at home.
- Repeat the directions for your partner.

Name _____ Date _____

Making Fraction Strips

Carefully cut each paper strip from this page. These strips will be used to fold fractions. Keep your finished strips in an envelope.

Name _____ Date _____

Making Fraction Strips

Carefully cut each paper strip from this page. These strips will be used to fold fractions. Keep your finished strips in an envelope.

Standard Frabble Cards

one-third	two-eighths	$\frac{4}{12}$	
Frabble	Frabble	Frabble	Frabble

$\frac{6}{8}$	six-twelfths		
Frabble	Frabble	Frabble	Frabble

	$\frac{1}{1}$		
Frabble	Frabble	Frabble	Frabble

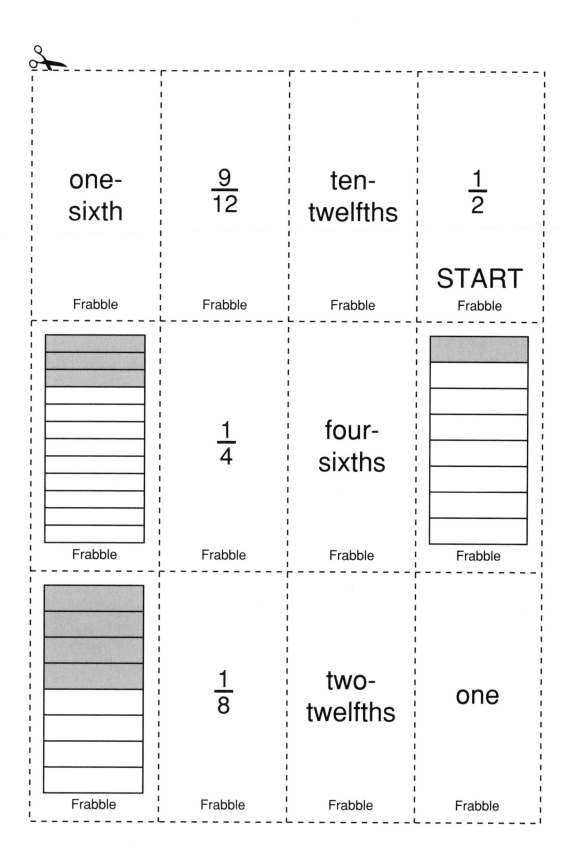

one-sixth	$\frac{9}{12}$	ten-twelfths	$\frac{1}{2}$
			START
Frabble	Frabble	Frabble	Frabble
	$\frac{1}{4}$	four-sixths	
Frabble	Frabble	Frabble	Frabble
	$\frac{1}{8}$	two-twelfths	one
Frabble	Frabble	Frabble	Frabble

Wild Cards for Frabble

✂

Wild Card	**Wild Card**	**Wild Card**	**Wild Card**
To play this card, you must name a fraction that is not on the board.	To play this card, you must name a fraction that is not on the board.	To play this card, you must name a fraction that is not on the board.	To play this card, you must name a fraction that is not on the board.
Frabble	Frabble	Frabble	Frabble
Wild Card	**Wild Card**	**Wild Card**	**Wild Card**
To play this card, you must name a fraction that is not on the board.	To play this card, you must name a fraction that is not on the board.	To play this card, you must name a fraction that is not on the board.	To play this card, you must name a fraction that is not on the board.
Frabble	Frabble	Frabble	Frabble

Challenge Frabble Cards

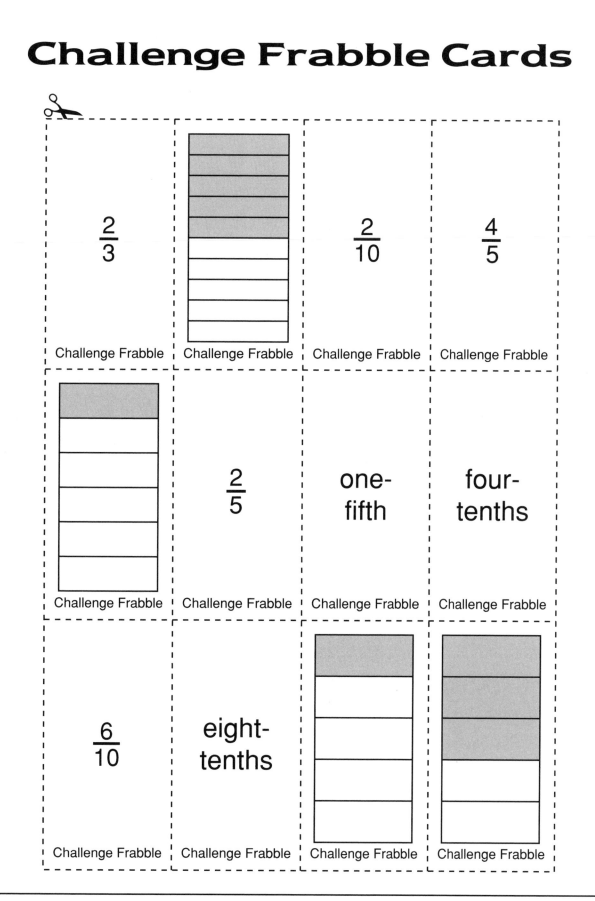

$\dfrac{2}{3}$		$\dfrac{2}{10}$	$\dfrac{4}{5}$
Challenge Frabble	Challenge Frabble	Challenge Frabble	Challenge Frabble
	$\dfrac{2}{5}$	one-fifth	four-tenths
Challenge Frabble	Challenge Frabble	Challenge Frabble	Challenge Frabble
$\dfrac{6}{10}$	eight-tenths		
Challenge Frabble	Challenge Frabble	Challenge Frabble	Challenge Frabble

Unit 13

Division

	Student Guide	Discovery Assignment Book	Adventure Book	Unit Resource Guide*
Lesson 1				
TV Survey				
Lesson 2				
Division				
Lesson 3				
More Division				
Lesson 4				
Solving Problems Using Multiplication and Division				
Lesson 5				
Plant Growth				

Unit Resource Guide pages are from the teacher materials.

Unit 13: Home Practice

Part 1 Triangle Flash Cards: Last Six Facts

Study for the quiz on the division facts for the last six facts (24 ÷ 6, 24 ÷ 4, 28 ÷ 7, 28 ÷ 4, 32 ÷ 8, 32 ÷ 4, 42 ÷ 7, 42 ÷ 6, 48 ÷ 8, 48 ÷ 6, 56 ÷ 8, 56 ÷ 7). Take home your *Triangle Flash Cards* and your list of facts you need to study.

Here's how to use the flash cards. Ask a family member to choose one flash card at a time. Your partner should cover the corner containing either the square or the circle. This number will be the answer to a division fact. Solve a division fact with the two uncovered numbers.

Your teacher will tell you when the quiz on these facts will be. Remember to study only those facts you cannot answer correctly and quickly.

Part 2 Working with Remainders

Show how you solved each of the following problems. Explain how any remainders affected your answer.

1. Nine cereal boxes fit into one crate. How many crates are needed for 30 boxes of cereal?

2. Twenty-one children try out for two teams. The children decided that anyone who is not selected will be an umpire. There are three umpires. How many children are on each of the two teams?

3. Mrs. Roberts collects a total of $273 from the 90 students who are going on a field trip. Each student brings in $3. Is the total of $273 the correct amount? Explain.

4. Irma wants to read her 453-page book in 9 days. If she reads about the same number of pages each night, how many should she read a night?

Part 3 Multiplication and Division Practice

Use paper and pencil or mental math to solve the following problems. If you need more work space to show your work, you may use a separate sheet of paper. Estimate to make sure your answers are reasonable.

1. **A.** $267 \times 7 =$ **B.** $78 \times 23 =$ **C.** $30 \times 58 =$ **D.** $73 \times 400 =$

     E. $6004 \times 8 =$ **F.** $269 \div 3 =$ **G.** $379 \div 2 =$ **H.** $467 \div 8 =$

2. Explain your estimation strategy for Question 1A.

Part 4 More Division Practice

Use paper and pencil or mental math to solve the following problems. Estimate to be sure your answers are reasonable.

   A. $3606 \div 6 =$ **B.** $4587 \div 7 =$ **C.** $6675 \div 5 =$ **D.** $855 \div 9 =$

Part 5 Create a Fraction

You may use your own fraction chart or the Fraction Chart in the *Student Guide* in Unit 12 Lesson 3 to help you solve these problems.

   A. Write a fraction that is larger than $\frac{1}{2}$, but smaller than $\frac{3}{4}$. _____

   B. Write a fraction that is a little bit smaller than $\frac{1}{8}$. _____

   C. Write a fraction that is double $\frac{1}{10}$. _____

   D. Write a fraction that is much larger than $\frac{1}{3}$, but smaller than $\frac{11}{12}$. _____

Part 6 Prizes

The children's hospital plans to spend $100 on stuffed animals for prizes for a raffle. The tiny ones are 10¢, the medium ones cost $2.00, and the large ones cost $5. They will buy some of each kind. (There are many solutions to this problem. If you need more work space, use a separate sheet of paper.)

   1. How many of each can they buy?

   2. What strategy or strategies did you use to solve this problem?

   3. How did you check your answer to see if it was correct?

   4. Show another solution to this problem.

Part 7 Solving Problems

Choose appropriate methods and tools to solve the following problems. Explain how you solved each problem.

1. Over a four-day period, Frank watched 325 minutes of TV. He watched 60 minutes of TV on Monday, 45 minutes on Tuesday, and 75 minutes on Wednesday.

    A. How many minutes did he watch on Thursday?

    B. About how many hours of TV did he watch on Thursday?

2. On Monday, Shannon watched 4 times the amount of TV as Luis. If Shannon watched TV for 180 minutes, how many minutes did Luis watch?

3. Mrs. Dewey watched 45 minutes of TV on Monday, 35 minutes on Tuesday, and 1 hour on Wednesday. She did not watch TV on Thursday. What is the mean number of minutes of TV watched by Mrs. Dewey over the four-day period?

4. Mrs. Randall's class watched a total of 5430 minutes of TV over a four-day period.

    A. Is this more or less than 50 hours of TV? How do you know?

    B. Is this more or less than 100 hours of TV? How do you know?

    C. Estimate the number of hours of TV the students in Mrs. Randall's class watched.

5. Mrs. Randall's class decided to change their TV habits. In a follow-up survey, the class watched a total of 3780 minutes of TV in four days.

    A. Did they watch more or less TV? How many minutes more or less?

    B. As a class, how many hours of TV did they cut out of their daily routine?

Triangle Flash Cards: Last Six Facts

- Work with a partner. Each partner cuts out the flash cards.
- To quiz you on a division fact, your partner covers the number in the square. Solve a division fact with the two uncovered numbers.
- Divide the used cards into three piles: those that you know and can answer quickly, those that you can figure out, and those that you need to learn.
- Practice the last two piles again. Then, make a list of the facts you need to practice at home.
- Go through the cards again. This time your partner covers the numbers in the circles.
- Sort the cards into the three piles. Make a list of the facts you need to practice at home.
- Repeat the directions for your partner.

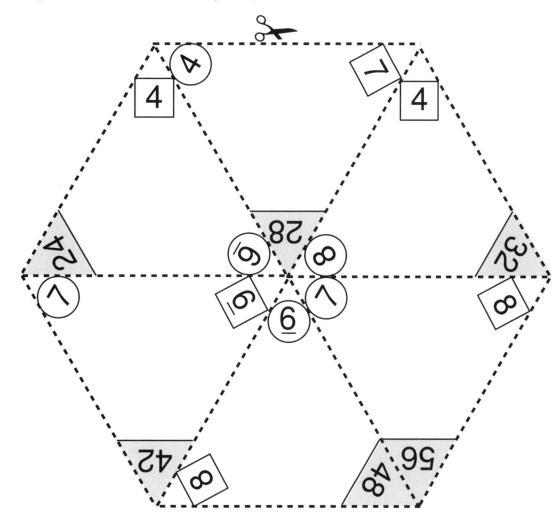

Daily TV Time

	Program	Starting Time	Ending Time	Minutes Watched
Day ___				

Total TV Minutes _____

	Program	Starting Time	Ending Time	Minutes Watched
Day ___				

Total TV Minutes _____

Program	Starting Time	Ending Time	Minutes Watched

Day _____

Total TV Minutes _____

Program	Starting Time	Ending Time	Minutes Watched

Day _____

Average Number of Minutes per Day _____

Average Number of Hours per Day _____

Total TV Minutes _____

Total Number of Minutes for 4 Days _____

How Much TV Do We Watch?

Average TV Time per Day (in hours)	Number of Students	
	Tallies	Total

Unit 14

Chancy Predictions: An Introduction to Probability

	Student Guide	Discovery Assignment Book	Adventure Book	Unit Resource Guide*
Lesson 1				
Chance Discussions	◉			
Lesson 2				
Bean Counter's Game	◉			
Lesson 3				
Rolling a Number Cube	◉			◉
Lesson 4				
From Number Cubes to Spinners	◉	◉		
Lesson 5				
Exploring Spinners	◉	◉		◉
Lesson 6				
Make Your Own Spinners	◉	◉		
Lesson 7				
Probe Quest			◉	

Unit Resource Guide pages are from the teacher materials.

Unit 14: Home Practice

Part 1 Triangle Flash Cards: 2s, 5s, 10s, and Square Numbers

Study for the quizzes on the division facts. Take home your *Triangle Flash Cards* and your list of facts you need to study.

Here's how to use the flash cards. Ask a family member to choose one flash card at a time. Your partner should cover the corner with the circle. This number will be the answer to a division fact, called the quotient. Use the two uncovered numbers to solve a division fact. Then have your partner go through the cards covering the corner with a square. Use the two uncovered numbers to solve a division fact.

Your teacher will tell you when the quiz on the facts will be. Remember to study only those facts you cannot answer correctly and quickly.

Part 2 School Supplies

The school store sells school supplies. The prices for notebooks, pencils, markers, and folders are shown.

spiral notebook	pencils	markers	folders
$0.39	4 for $1.00	$2.98	10 for $1.00

Jessie bought 4 spiral notebooks, 1 set of markers, 8 folders, and 10 pencils.

Jacob bought 5 spiral notebooks, 1 set of markers, 10 folders, and 5 pencils.

Choose an appropriate method to solve each of the following problems. For each question, you may choose to use paper and pencil, mental math, or a calculator. Be prepared to explain how you solved each problem. Use a separate sheet of paper to show your work.

1. Figure out the exact cost of each student's supplies.

2. Whose supplies cost the most?

3. What is the difference in price between the two students' supplies?

4. Choose one of the students' lists and explain how you figured out the total. What was the hardest part of the problem? Why?

Part 3 Multiplication and Division Practice

Use paper and pencil or mental math to solve the following problems. If you need more work space to show your work, you may use a separate sheet of paper. Estimate to make sure your answers are reasonable.

A. $945 \times 5 =$ **B.** $302 \times 7 =$ **C.** $99 \times 99 =$ **D.** $6 \times 3274 =$

E. $1342 \times 7 =$ **F.** $1735 \div 5 =$ **G.** $9276 \div 2 =$ **H.** $738 \div 8 =$

I. $9987 \div 6 =$ **J.** $1258 \div 3 =$ **K.** $2232 \div 4 =$ **L.** $9900 \div 9 =$

M. Choose one of the above questions and explain your strategy for estimation.

N. Choose another of the above questions and explain your strategy for mental math.

Part 4 Probability Lines

Use letters to place the following events on the probability line below.

Probability Line

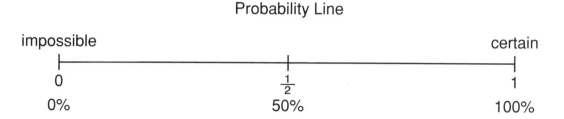

A. Romesh will be the next president of the United States.

B. A spinner is evenly divided into four colors: red, blue, green, and yellow. In one spin, it will land on green.

C. You will travel to Europe next year.

D. Martians will invade the planet this afternoon.

E. A coin flip will land on heads.

F. It will rain tomorrow.

G. There will be seven days in next week.

H. The sidewalk in front of the school is concrete.

I. A dog will have kittens.

J. You will win the lottery today.

Part 5 The Power of 10

Use paper and pencil, not a calculator, for these problems.

A. What patterns do you notice in the problems?

B. What pattern do you think you will see in the answers?

C. 832×6 D. 832×60 E. 832×600 F. 832×6000

G. 759×6 H. 759×60 I. 759×600 J. 759×6000

K. Arrange your answers from smallest to largest.

Part 6 Movie Library

Solve the following problems using appropriate tools. Explain how you solved each problem.

1. Michael, Shannon, and Jessie decided to create a movie library for their neighborhood. They asked parents and teachers to donate children's videos to create a library. Neighborhood residents could take out a children's movie for free if they brought one in as a trade. In the first week of the drive to collect movies, Michael collected 17 boxes. Each box was filled with 22 movies. How many movies did Michael collect?

2. Shannon collected 11 boxes with 27 movies in each. How many movies did Shannon collect?

3. Jessie and her friends collected 36 boxes with 15 movies in each. How many movies did they collect?

4. Approximately, how many movies did Michael, Shannon, and Jessie collect in all?

5. Jessie's little brother likes to watch the same video over and over. If the video lasts 39 minutes and he watched it 8 times in one week, about how many hours did he spend watching the video?

6. In all, 8 children worked in the movie library on Saturday. If each child helped about 30 neighborhood residents check out one movie, about how many movies were checked out on Saturday?

A Spinner for a Number Cube

With a partner, use the outline below to create a spinner which gives the same results as a number cube. Use a protractor to help you.

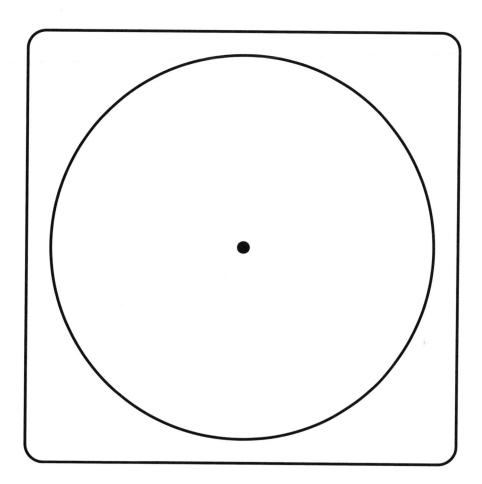

Exploring Spinners 1 and 2

Spinner 1

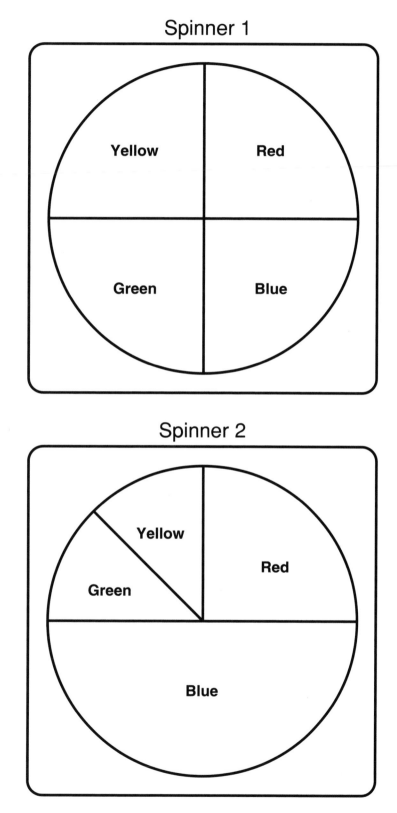

Spinner 2

Blank Spinners

Make Your Own Spinners

Unit 15
Using Patterns

	Student Guide	Discovery Assignment Book	Adventure Book	Unit Resource Guide*
Lesson 1				
Plant Growth Conclusion	◎	◎		
Lesson 2				
In the Shade of the Old Meranpi Tree			◎	
Lesson 3				
Planet Gzorp	◎			◎
Lesson 4				
Function Machines	◎			
Lesson 5				
Taste of TIMS	◎			◎
Lesson 6				
Patterns and Problems	◎			

Unit Resource Guide pages are from the teacher materials.

Unit 15: Home Practice

Part 1 Triangle Flash Cards: 3s, 9s, Last Six Facts

Study for the two quizzes on the division facts. Half the facts will be on the first quiz. The other half will be on the second quiz. Take home your *Triangle Flash Cards* and your list of facts you need to study.

Here's how to use the flash cards. Ask a family member to choose one flash card at a time. Your partner should cover the corner with a square. This number will be the answer to a division fact. Divide the two uncovered numbers. Go through cards again, but this time cover the number in the circle.

Your teacher will tell you when the quizzes on the facts will be. Remember to study only those facts you cannot answer correctly and quickly.

Part 2 Mixed-Up Multiplication Tables

1. Complete the tables.

A.

×	3	4	6	7	8
4					
6		24			
7					
8					

B.

×	0	1	5	7	9
3					
6			30		
9					
10					

2. Solve each fact. Then, on a separate sheet of paper, name three other facts that are in the same fact family. For example, the following four facts are in the same fact family: $3 \times 6 = 18$, $6 \times 3 = 18$, $18 \div 3 = 6$, and $18 \div 6 = 3$. (Remember, the square numbers only have two facts in each family.)

A. $8 \times 4 =$ _____   B. $81 \div 9 =$ _____   C. $7 \times 6 =$ _____

D. $9 \times 4 =$ _____   E. $21 \div 7 =$ _____   F. $10 \times 9 =$ _____

G. $3 \times 3 =$ _____   H. $56 \div 7 =$ _____   I. $6 \times 9 =$ _____

Name _____ Date _____

Part 3 Practicing the Operations

On a separate sheet of paper, solve the following problems using paper and pencil or mental math. Estimate to make sure your answers are reasonable.

1. A. $546 + 89 =$ _____   B. $3438 - 723 =$ _____

   C. $2905 + 376 =$ _____   D. $79 \times 5 =$ _____

   E. $2306 \times 8 =$ _____   F. $347 \div 5 =$ _____

   G. $62 \times 40 =$ _____   H. $5073 - 782 =$ _____

   I. $9540 \div 6 =$ _____   J. $504 \div 9 =$ _____

   K. $1789 + 4532 =$ _____   L. $6730 - 762 =$ _____

   M. $29 \times 44 =$ _____   N. $4003 \div 7 =$ _____

2. Explain your strategy for Question 1D.

Part 4 Telling Time

1. What time is it? _____

2. What time will it be in 3 hours? _____

3. What time was it 45 minutes ago? _____

4. What time will it be in $1\frac{1}{2}$ hours? _____

5. What time was it 90 minutes ago? _____

6. Jacob's grandmother is coming to Chicago for a visit. Her plane takes off in Florida at 11:30 A.M. It will take her about 45 minutes to get to the airport. If she wants to arrive at the airport about $1\frac{1}{2}$ hours before take-off, what time should she leave her home?

7. Irma's brother is in high school. He has four 55-minute classes before lunch. If his first class starts at 8:05 and there are 5 minutes between each class, what time is his lunch period? Show how you decided.

Good and Bad Experiments

1. Jacob wants to see if the volume of the dirt in the cup affects how tall a plant grows. He does the experiment shown below.

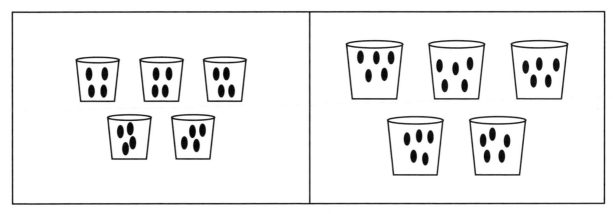

Volume of dirt = 100 cc   Volume of dirt = 300 cc

Is this a good experiment to find out whether the volume of dirt will affect the height of the plant? Explain.

2. Jacob changes his experiment as shown below. Will the experiment now show how the volume of dirt affects plant height? Explain.

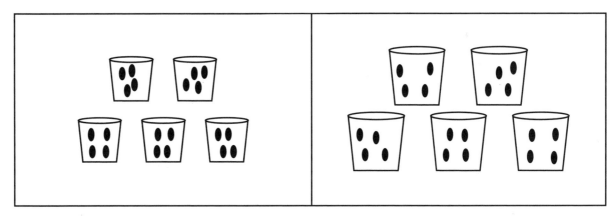

Volume of dirt = 100 cc   Volume of dirt = 300 cc

Unit 16

Assessing Our Learning

	Student Guide	Discovery Assignment Book	Adventure Book	Unit Resource Guide*
Lesson 1				
Experiment Review	🌀	🌀		
Lesson 2				
Problems and Practice	🌀			
Lesson 3				
Area vs. Length	🌀			
Lesson 4				
The Many-Eyed Dragonfly				🌀
Lesson 5				
End-of-Year Test				🌀
Lesson 6				
Portfolios	🌀			

Unit Resource Guide pages are from the teacher materials.

Unit 16: Home Practice

Part 1 Triangle Flash Cards: All the Facts

Study for the test on all the division facts. Take home your *Triangle Flash Cards* and your list of facts you need to study.

Here's how to use the flash cards. Ask a family member to choose one flash card at a time. Your partner should cover the corner containing the number in a square. This number will be the answer to a division fact. Solve a division fact with the two uncovered numbers. Go through the cards a second time, this time covering the numbers in the circle.

Your teacher will tell you when the test on all the facts will be. Remember to concentrate on those facts you cannot answer correctly and quickly.

Part 2 Multiplication Tables

Complete the following tables.

1.

×	7	4	6	2	9
8					
3	12				
5					
1					

2.

×	10	5	6	3	0
8					
4		20			
2					
1					

3. Complete the following. Remember to follow the correct order of operations. Do all multiplications before any addition and subtraction. For example,
$4 + 100 \times 3 =$
$4 + 300 = 304.$

A. $7 \times 100 + 3 =$ _____

B. $6 + 800 \times 7 =$ _____

C. $5000 - 400 \times 5 =$ _____

D. $20 \times 20 + 350 =$ _____

E. $600 \times 80 - 2000 =$ _____

F. $20,000 - 18,000 \times 1 =$ _____

Part 3 Symmetry

Use the figure below to answer the following questions.

1. Does the figure have turn symmetry? If so, what kind? (*Hint:* Does it have $\frac{1}{2}$-turn symmetry, $\frac{1}{3}$-turn symmetry, $\frac{1}{4}$-turn symmetry, or $\frac{1}{6}$-turn symmetry?)

2. Does this shape have line symmetry? If so, draw in the lines of symmetry.

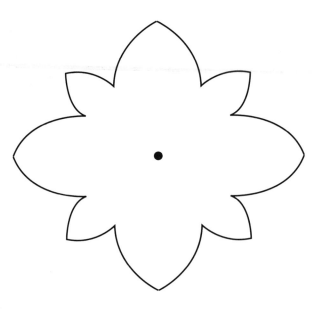

Part 4 Fractions and Decimals

Complete the following table. ⬭ **is one whole.**

Base-Ten Shorthand	Decimal	Fraction
⬭⬭⬭//		
	4.03	
	10.41	
⬭⬭⬭⬭/ ···		

ASSESSING OUR LEARNING

Name _____   Date _____

Part 5 School Days

Use the data below to answer the following questions.

Country	Average Number of School Days
U.S.A.	180
Canada	186
England	192
Japan	243

1. About how many days will a child in England have gone to school when he or she has attended school for 5 years?

2. Yoshi lives in Japan. He has gone to school for 5 years. Jackie lives in the United States. She has gone to school for 5 years. About how many more days has Yoshi gone to school than Jackie?

3. About how many days does a student in the U.S.A. have to go to school to graduate from high school? (To graduate from high school, most students must go to school for 13 years.)

Part 6 Multiplication and Division Practice

Solve the following problems using paper and pencil or mental math. Show your work on a separate sheet of paper. Estimate to make sure your answers are reasonable. Explain your estimation strategy for D.

A. $64 \times 77 =$ _____   B. $23 \times 48 =$ _____

C. $70 \times 56 =$ _____   D. $3540 \times 4 =$ _____

E. $875 \div 7 =$ _____   F. $5960 \div 6 =$ _____

G. $3000 \div 50 =$ _____   H. $7812 \div 9 =$ _____

Part 7 Function Machines

1. Complete the following tables.

A.

Input N	Output 3 + 2 × N
1	5
2	
3	
4	
5	
6	
7	
8	

B.

Input N	Output 5 × N
1	5
2	
3	
4	
5	
6	
7	
8	

2. Nicholas predicted that the outputs would be the same for both data tables. Are they the same? Why or why not?

Part 8 Downhill Racer

You will need a piece of *Centimeter Graph Paper.*

1. John rolled a car down a ramp at three different heights. At each height he took three trials. The data here shows the average distance (in cm) the car rolled at each height. Graph the data on *Centimeter Graph Paper.*

2. If the points form a line, fit a line to the points.

3. Predict the distance the car will roll if the height of the ramp is 30 cm.

Downhill Racer

Height (in cm)	Average Distance (in cm)
8	100
16	198
24	305

Experiment Review Chart

Directions:
- Write the names of the experiments completed this year in the first row of the table.
- Complete each column with information from each lab.

Name of Experiment → / Experiment Elements ↓			
Main Variables			
Fixed Variables			
Anything Measured (units)			
Number of Trials			
Type of Graph			
Important Questions (Answers may vary.)			

Name _____   Date _____

Directions:
- Write the names of the experiments completed this year in the first row of the table.
- Complete each column with information from each lab.

Name of Experiment → Experiment Elements ↓			
Main Variables			
Fixed Variables			
Anything Measured (units)			
Number of Trials			
Type of Graph			
Important Questions (Answers may vary.)			